A VETERAN'S HOW TO GUIDE

Regarding Obtaining Veteran's Disability Benefits,
Dealing with Clinical Psychological Disorders
And
Problematic Stress Responses

(2nd Edition)

ANNE AND BILL BOWMAN

A Veteran's How-to Guide:
Regarding Obtaining Veteran's Disability Benefits,
Dealing with Clinical Psychological Disorders
And
Problematic Stress Responses
Copyright © 2017 by Anne and Bill Bowman

Library of Congress Control Number: 2017945588
ISBN-13:   Paperback: 978-1-64045-609-9
            PDF: 978-1-64045-612-9
            ePub: 978-1-64045-611-2
            Kindle: 978-1-64045-613-6
            Hardcover: 978-1-64045-610-5

Printed in the United States of America

LitFire
PUBLISHING

LitFire LLC
1-800-511-9787
www.litfirepublishing.com
order@litfirepublishing.com

CONTENTS

A Prayer for the Military

Almighty Father, bless and protect all the men and women serving in the United States Armed Forces. Guide and direct them in defense of the United States of America and in the maintenance of justice throughout the world.

Blessed are those who stand in the tradition of Joshua and who follow orders to protect people against evil forces. (Joshua 1:1–9, paraphrase KJV)

We must always remember that God promised that HE will never abandon us or fail to help us. By asking God to direct us, we can conquer many of life's challenges and at all times we must put our trust in You (God); through Jesus Christ our Lord and Savior, Amen.

This prayer was created by: Chaplains Anne and Bill Bowman

DEDICATION

This book is dedicated to all of the military nurses who have served with dignity and dedication and have gone unrecognized for too long. Their valiant service through times of personal danger to save the servicemen they were caring for helped so many of them survive. Enough cannot be said for the nurses. Thank you from all of us who have served in the military.

INTRODUCTION

"For surely there is an end and thine expectation shall not be cut off."
Proverbs 23:18 KJV

This is the second edition of "A Veteran's How-To Guide." The contents cover obtaining veteran's disability benefits, dealing with clinical psychological disorders and problematic stress responses and many other processes that you will be introduced to in your travel through the Dept. of Veterans Affairs system. It is important to understand that before you travel down this bumpy road of the government processes.

The Department of Veterans Affairs regulations change with each new Administration in Washington D.C. This book will assist you in maneuvering through the processes and appeal system when you are denied your benefits that you earned as a veteran.

The Federal Department of Veterans Affairs and the State Department of Veterans Affairs are also located in each state as a free service for the veteran. Both Departments are on line and will also provide veteran's resource books at no cost.

The American veteran swore to defend this country and to be willing to give his or her life. All veterans, upon entering the military, are required to take an oath to the United States of America. The words, "So help me God," are written into the oath.

Tis book was written with the intent to guide veterans (whether they were in combat or not) through a process established by the Department of Veterans Affairs (DVA), Disability Benefits and Pension Qualification System when applying for veteran's disability benefits. The process was developed to be long termed, time delaying, misdirecting and frustrating. It can be said that the DVA wants all supportive documentation, every emotion evaluated, medical examination and historical data that can be presented by the veteran and/or by outside sources.

Every person who applies will need a support team, a knowledgeable Veteran Service Officer (VSO), and faith in God. These aforementioned items and this research paper will provide the tools to get through the DVA disability process in a time efficient and less frustrating manner.

Throughout this book there are a number of Biblical Scriptures chosen to assist the reader in becoming, and staying, motivated and maintaining a peace of mind through faith and a trust in God.

Consider the DVA Disability process as a combat situation and you are under fire. It is at that point in time when you learn the meaning of, *"There are no atheists in a fox hole."*

I am a disabled combat veteran of a foreign war who is directing the information in this book to civilians, and to veterans in particular. The emotional problems discussed in this book cover symptoms that can be related to veteran stressors (war related) as well civilian stressors.

Most people are unaware that they have emotional problems, or that they may be in a state of emotional denial.

All the veterans, and their families, entering a claim for disability benefits need know is to be prepared for an uphill battle. My personal experiences, which were written about in this book, should help relieve individuals of some frustrations and enable them to get their benefits in a more expedient manner. I received my disability benefits from the Department of Veterans Affairs, but not without a 3-year fight which included two appeals and daily prayer.

The veterans who are requesting and applying for veteran benefits, because of their emotional or physical ailments, are facing a long and demeaning process. This guide will provide a step-by-step method for obtaining their VA benefits, eliminate some frustrations and provide, through Biblical Scriptures, a calming force through faith in God.

The format in developing this book is simple. The format is also people- friendly while maintaining wording that all people can understand when discussing physical and emotional problems and the government disability processes. You will have to repeat yourself when answering to the Department of Veterans Affairs. You must always tell the truth and have documents to back your statements. When you are required to appeal, again, you will be asked to repeat yourself … Get used to it!

ACKNOWLEDGEMENT "THROUGH THE EYES OF THE WIFE"

Now Faith is the substance of things hoped for, the evidence of things not seen.
Hebrews 11:1 KJV

But if we hope for what we see not, then do we with patience wait for it.
Romans 8:25 KJV

This acknowledgement is for the spouses of the military who proudly served in the wars fought by the United States of America to keep our country free. Those spouses are also combatants in a different kind of war.

You would think that, after all of the sacrifices that a veteran made for the sake of his/her country, the government would bend over backwards to compensate them for any injuries incurred in the line of duty. Wrong!! What this country does to its veterans is unconscionable. The veteran gave his time, and frequently his life, to defend his country in times of need, whatever the cause. However, upon discharge, the end of his assigned service often leads to the real beginning of his battle.

There is no way for the spouse of a veteran to prepare for the battle that is coming. Make no mistake. There will be a battle when the vet comes home! The battle will either be waged with the government, or it will be waged with the people closest to him in his life. Face it, whenever there is a personal problem there are only two ways to handle it. It will either be internalized in some way, or externalized in some way. Either way there will be repercussions. The best thing that the spouse can do is be there, be supportive, be patient and seek ways to turn the negatives into positives. All the while, pray and ask the Lord for help and guidance.

When my husband, Bill Bowman, began his quest for his veteran's benefits, he had no idea that was the beginning of another war. Even before his VA disability papers were originally submitted, he was told by more than one "successful" veteran (one who had received his benefits) to be prepared to be denied. I was astounded! What a great way to find out that the government you supported was not going to support you. The veterans, who had already fought this battle, and "won", told him exactly what would happen, and it happened exactly that way. It often takes years for the veteran to "successfully win" his battle with the government and begin to collect his benefits. In Bill's case, his first "victory" came two years after his battle started.

Efficiency in administration was definitely not a key factor for the veterans. When Bill went to make his appointment, he was told that it would not be possible to see the psychiatrist for three months. However, he was blessed and, as it happened, an appointment became available within two weeks.

Of course, he took that appointment without hesitation! Obviously, that did help to speed the whole process he was facing, even though it was, and is, a process of hurry up and wait. For reasons that have nothing to do with this process, Bill was not working at this time. That turned out to be most fortuitous, because you are expected to be available for any and all appointments, without regard to your own obligations. If you miss an appointment, regardless of the reason, you go to the bottom of the list and have to start all over again. In a most impersonal way, appointments are made for you and then sent in a letter to you, often within a day or two of the actual appointment.

He knew that after he submitted his papers he would be denied, and it happened exactly as he was told it would. However, as is his habit, he made sure that when he submitted his original papers all questions were answered in simple English, and that no questions were skipped. He thought for sure that no-one would deny him, because the case was so obvious. After all, he had spent time in military hospitals for his mental condition, and those stays were documented in his military medical records. Unfortunately, that is true only when the organization is there for you, and that is not the case here. Because of Bill's style, the psychiatrist, the first doctor that he met, could tell that he had PTSD, (post-traumatic stress disorder), and so noted in his notes. When Bill asked him how he could tell so fast, he said that his answers to the questions were so detailed that he had left him no additional questions to ask. Bill felt validated, finally, that a qualified VA doctor established that he did, indeed, have PTSD. Even though he had spent time in a military hospital for stress related problems while serving in Viet Nam, he still felt he needed this validation, and vindication.

Since he knew that he was going to be denied, he was mentally prepared when that did occur. He continued to follow the advice he received. He submitted his appeal immediately because he was told that the appeal process would take a year, so he wanted to start the process as soon as possible.

As I watched him proceed with this part of the process, I was so grateful that he was blessed with outstanding critical thinking skills, as well as excellent writing skills. As an educator, I knew the value of those skills but, at that point, I had no idea how important they would become.

How sad is that? At first, I couldn't, or wouldn't, believe it, because I had this naïve view that the government was there for its people, especially its veterans who gave so much to preserve the freedoms we hold dear. As I watched my husband fight for his benefits, I realized he was actually fighting against the United States Government for something that should have been given to him without question. As the process continued to unfold, I realized that the government really had no intention to pay anything to anyone, and was set up to make things as difficult as possible if benefits were to be eventually awarded. I was stunned, and completely disillusioned. I began to understand why so many veterans were homeless, and/or had committed suicide. They were actually treated with both disrespect and disdain, by the very government they had sworn to protect. Let's be honest here. The general public is not well equipped to think critically, or write well, so why should the average veteran be any different? Consequently, they were treated with that attitude.

When my husband first began the process of obtaining his benefits, he was given a myriad of forms to fill out, and was told that he would need to be examined for whatever his ailments were. Since he had to be examined by a VA doctor, he proceeded to make his appointments. He had a long list of war wounds that were still evident after so many years. Before he even got confirmation from the myriad of doctors that he would eventually see, he knew he had an indentation in his left thigh from a bad jeep accident, severely pronated ankles, knee problems from the jeep accident and the pronation, tinnitus, diabetes, hypertension, black toe fungus and jungle rot in the crotch. Needless to say, he made all of that information very clear on all the forms he filled out. I don't think that there is a veteran who comes home who does not have PTSD. It is just a natural by-product of war, among other things. Since one of his war wounds was PTSD, he needed to see the only psychiatrist that serviced the veterans at the VA Hospital in the San Fernando Valley in Southern California. Nothing would proceed without seeing this doctor first. The first thing that occurred to me at that point was that the system was definitely set up to cause stress, for both the doctor as well as the veterans. How could only one doctor possibly service the needs of so many veterans? It just wasn't possible, without causing problems somewhere, somehow.

I was on the sidelines, watching a highly educated man fight with this cumbersome, maze-like process. I could not imagine what a person with little to no education would do, or could do. The whole process is set up with obstacles to cause enough problems so as to make most veterans just give up and quit. Unfortunately, it is working, because far less veterans end up getting their benefits than started the process. Once he had all the forms in his hands, he began to read them so he could fill them out completely and correctly. That is just the way he does things. As he started this process, I watched him as he began to relive all the horrors of a war that he had "successfully" buried many years ago. The Viet Nam war was terrible, on all levels, but Bill had the distinction of being in the 3rd Marine Division which fought near the DMZ during 1967-68. He survived the Tet Offensive, and now I had to watch him begin to relive it all over again.

I was aghast that the government would purposefully do this to its vets, and as the process continued my perception of my country's government became so much more cynical and much less trusting. I began to realize that, from the government's perspective, it was just a matter of money. The more the veterans could be put off for any reason, real or imagined, the less money the government would have to pay out to the very people who had guaranteed its existence. It didn't really care how much the veterans gave, how much suffering they went through. Any veteran who was going to get money was going to have to relive the hell they had experienced to get there. If they didn't have PTSD before this horrific process started, (which would have been impossible since PTSD is an inherent side-effect of war), then they were sure to have it as this process progressed. There really is no light at the end of this tunnel, because it is more like a maze with no way out. Bill's paper work was just shuffled around on the desk of an incompetent counselor until he took matters into his own hands. He did eventually change things and got a very competent counselor, someone who was not only supportive, but also a good guide for whatever was to come next.

I watched as Bill filed all his papers, went to all of his doctor's appointments, and stayed in touch with his counselor, knowing full well that he was going to be denied, and denied he was. The process that he started in January 2003, ended with a denial in September 2003. When he did receive his letter from the VA board, it actually stated that his benefits would be denied because he was not in a combat zone. Not in a combat zone!!! What part of Viet Nam was recreational at that time?! We were dumbfounded, and I honestly did not know whether to laugh or cry. When Bill told me that the members of the board were not required to be former military, I then understood the foolishness of the answers. Only a fool, or a poorly trained board member, would say that you could be in Viet Nam and not be in a combat zone. Again, in deference to the national budget, the board, which had once been comprised of the military, was now made up of layman whose experience of war was, in many cases, non-existent. What made them qualified to pass judgment on injuries incurred in the military? The answer is nothing. Consequently, foolish and ignorant answers were put in writing to the veterans applying for their benefits. As I said before, because the average person is not well educated, most of the veterans who were turned down accepted that response as final. Fortunately, Bill is highly educated, and highly trained to think critically. Consequently, when Bill received his letter of rejection, he was ready for the next step. He immediately appealed, and his appeal letter included more DOD statistics and information than anyone wanted to read. (Overkill is another sign of PTSD.) However, all of that information was relevant to show a non-military board member how his injuries were war related.

He sent in his letter of appeal, and the required disagreements, and knew that it would take another year for him to get a decision, because that is what the rules said. Since he knew that the government set up deadlines that it was ill prepared to meet, he actively prepared for his next step. For him, this second year was up on September 9, 2004, and as the clock struck midnight, he was locked and loaded! We both knew that the mail would not bring the long-anticipated letter telling him that his benefits would start, even though that is what we prayed for on a daily basis. Consequently, I watched the man who had patiently "waited" for an additional year, according to protocol, shift into high gear. When I asked him, more than once, why he was waiting, he told me just to be patient. He was playing "the game" by the rules of the opponent, because he knew that the only way to win. He made the saying "Given enough rope you will hang yourself" come to life. My husband is a master at playing chess, and I was watching him play it with the government.

While he was waiting for "that year" to pass, I was watching an amazingly strong man have to relive all of the effects of a war that no-one wanted. Here I am talking about Viet Nam, as well as the one he was fighting now with his own government. It was reasonable to assume that what was happening was right, because the government was doing it. Consequently, Bill did not find out that the way he was discharged from the Marines was really abnormal, probably because of the political atmosphere of the time. That the Viet Nam war was a very unpopular war would be an understatement. However, as many other men of those times did, Bill went to war because he was dedicated to serving the country as did his father before him. He chose to be a Marine because he believed in what they did. Unfortunately, the country was politically divided over that war. I remember so clearly that our military men were not given a warm greeting when they arrived home. They were spit on and ridiculed by the very people who enjoyed their democratic rights, but were not willing to fight for them.

The way the military was "greeted" upon their return was abhorrent, and he was not treated much differently by the government. When he was finally discharged from the Marines, in November 1968, he went through a very short military de-briefing. That de-briefing included a very short orientation on civilian life, and his military records were never discussed with him. Very traumatically, he went from fighting for his life in the war to fighting for his life, and his livelihood, at home in Los Angeles in ten days. This de-briefing gave him no preparation for what he was about to experience. The Marines were told to take off their uniforms when they left the base, for their own protection. He was told that he might be attacked, or spit upon by civilians. Bill refused! The trauma of fighting in Viet Nam, coupled with the horror of an unwelcoming, antagonistic America, just exacerbated the unrecognized cycle of PTSD.

All I could do was watch as Bill, once again, had to relive the horrors of the war just to fill out all of the papers he was given. He managed to do that, and keep his head on straight, which was no mean feat. He did have a couple of day where he had a major meltdown, and there was nothing I could do for him but to just be there. I felt totally helpless, and all I could do was watch as he battled his way back to normalcy. I marveled at his mental strength, as he talked his way out of the minefield of his mind. I was in awe, and knew that if he could do it then I could too, when the time came.

In the interim, he also became painfully aware that the counselor with who he had begun his claim was simply not capable of dealing with his responsibilities. That particular man was truly incompetent, and, as is Bill's style, he used that to his advantage. That counselor was one of the most negative, degrading, humiliating men Bill had ever come across, and worked diligently, at their first meeting, to talk Bill out of filing for as much as he could. When he came home from that meeting he knew he was in for a battle, but he just didn't know how big. He knew that he would have to change counselors, and he did that with aplomb at just the right time. He gave that counselor enough rope, and he did hang himself. Bill really did not have to say anything negative at all. When he wrote a letter to the DVA explaining why he wanted to change counselors, all he had to do by then was to list all of what had taken place. He was very complementary to his new counselor, his manager, and had nothing to say, at all, about the old counselor. By omission, he said it all. All of that took place while he was waiting for that second year to pass. According to the government book of rules, this decision should be made within a year. He had to wait for that year to pass entirely if he was going to play the game by the rules that were established. That was the only way to win.

During the second year, as he was patiently waiting for it to pass, he was busy accumulating all of the papers that had to fill out, responses he wrote, statistics he accumulated for his answers, and mail that he had received and made a notebook of them. Everything was in order, and so was he. I was stunned when he read what the instructions were for the appeal. When he was doing his research, and studying the procedures of the Department of Veterans Affairs Board, he found their 7-step program. The first statement read that the veteran should get a lawyer. The government was actually telling the vet that they were ready to fight, rather than pay benefits. By this time, I was no longer able to feel any emotions at all. I had already begun to realize that the veterans are not in the ruling class, and there was no way that the government was a friend to anyone without money. Bill could see the handwriting on the wall, and skipped that step entirely. He went directly to the state government, and turned it upon itself. He took the time to write an introduction to this "book" that he had created. He took the time to make 5 DVD's of himself in war, made from film that was actually taken of him during the war while he was under attack near the DMZ. He took the time to go to Kinko's and have 5 bound copies of this 30-page document of his experiences made, including the DVD, and a written narrative of it. He took the time to get the appropriate addresses for two congressmen, two state senators and the governor, and then he took the time to mail them. Then he sat back and waited, and so did I. By this time all I could do was marvel at how he was playing the game, and I waited for the next move.

Let's see now. This second year was up in September 2004, and those documents were mailed by the beginning of October 2004. We knew "stuff" was hitting the fan, because of how fast things began to happen. Bill received a letter from one congressman, who informed him that, unfortunately, he was not in his district but that he would mail it on to "our" congressman. He wished Bill good luck. Our congressman now had two copies of the document, but I don't remember that he ever responded to Bill. However, Bill did hear from the senators who had received his package. One simply said that she would forward it on to the California Department of Veterans Affairs, which I immediately felt would do nothing since that is where all the problems stem from. The other senator actually had a person on her staff to handle veteran's affairs, and that liaison actually did call Bill. I felt as if that was a major victory, and it was. They had a good conversation, and she is the one who informed him that his package had started a congressional investigation. We celebrated that bittersweet victory. It seemed almost sacrilegious to celebrate a victory against your own government, even though it had been set up that way. Bill also eventually received a letter from the governor's office as well, though by that time things were well on their way. The Governor's office also sent him a letter advising him that they were also investigating the matter, and it was ultimately sent to the VA headquarters on Wilshire Blvd. in Los Angeles.

We really had no idea what to expect next. Each time the postman visited us, another surprise was delivered, or so it seemed. Right after Thanksgiving, Bill received two letters from the VA giving him three appointments in two days to see outside doctors regarding his stated injuries on his claims. Again, no-one asked if those were convenient for you, or if you drive. They just expected you to be there, and there we were. Those appointments were scheduled for December 13 and 14, 2004. All of a sudden things were beginning to happen, and we were really excited. Each of those appointments addressed another issue, and we were even given a small check each time to reimburse us for mileage.

That was an unexpected "windfall", which added up to $10.74. Each time we went, Bill asked when the doctor's papers would be submitted. He was told they would be submitted that day, but after that who knows.

Then, on the last day of the year, in the last mail of the year, a big, fat letter came from the VA, explaining that Bill had been awarded 30% for his PTSD! How fast was that?! It took from mid-October until December 31, 2004, only because the politicians were brought into the situation. The letter also went on to state that his claim for his tinnitus, hearing loss and diabetes were deferred pending the reading of the doctor's evaluations. They had "taken care of business" so fast that they did not even wait for their own doctor's evaluations on these three issues. Obviously, all they wanted to do was to get Bill off their back. It was as if this was "shut up and go away" money.

Granted, that was only my take on the situation. The truth is that I was full of mixed emotions, and I really did not know how to feel. One obvious reaction was exhilaration because Bill had "won" in, what I considered to be, a completely unnecessary battle with his own government. Quite obviously, I am not a politician, and am not tied into any pay-back situation. I am a firm believer that if you earn something, as every veteran has done, you should be paid for your sacrifices. At least now we both knew that the process had been started. When payments do eventually start, the first check is retroactive back to the date that the original papers were filed. He received a retroactive check for his PTSD only, at 30%, and will be receiving a monthly, tax free pension check for that only for the rest of his life. Even though I was elated that the process had begun, another emotion I was feeling was surprise that he received an incomplete evaluation. I gave the powers that be far too much credit at being efficient at what they do. Another was disappointment knowing that Bill was going to have to continue his fight to get full compensation for what the government had either deferred or denied. Yet another was total exasperation. I was happy for us, but I knew that most of the veterans the government was trying to deny did not have the skills or motivation to continue the good fight. They needed help!

The letter Bill received was four pages long, and actually contradicted itself between statements from the first page to the last page. I really couldn't figure out if it was poorly dictated, poorly typed or brilliantly done to confuse the recipient. I eventually came to the conclusion that the first two choices were correct, and the third was an accidental by-product of sheer incompetence. I have to tell you that my perspective of our government's support has really been adversely impacted by this whole experience. Granted, I would not want to live anywhere else in the world, but I can think of a few things that I would like to see changed, and the treatment of our veterans is one of them.

Amazingly, on Valentine's Day, February 14, 2005 Bill received a phone call from a member of the VA board asking him what he wanted because his package to the government had caused such havoc.

Bill said that all he wanted was to be fairly compensated for his injuries. He was awarded 100 % shortly after that conversation.

Written by Anne Bowman

CHAPTER 1

Look before you leap

Thou therefore, my son, be strong in the grace that is in Christ Jesus. And the things that thou hast heard of me among many witnesses the same commit thou to faithful men who shall be able to teach others also. Thou therefore endure hardness, as a good soldier of Jesus Christ. No man that wareth entangleth himself with the affairs of this life, that he may please him who hath chosen him to be a soldier. And if a man also strive for masteries yet is he not crowned except he strive lawfully the husbandman that laboreth must be first partaker of the fruits. Consider what I say; and the Lord give thee understanding in all things.
2 Timothy 2:1–7 KJV

Have not I commanded thee? Be strong and of good courage; be not afraid neither be thou dismayed: for the Lord thy God is with thee whithersoever thou goest.
Joshua 1:9 KJV

This is a "How to Guide" on how to fight for your veteran's disability benefits. Why am I writing this book? I am writing this book because I am proud to be an American who served in the military during the Vietnam War. I have been involved in the process of trying to obtain the disability benefits I earned. Basically, I am concerned with a government system that spends more time delaying, blocking, frustrating and misdirecting millions of proud American Veterans who served their country, the United States of America, than in helping them. When going through the process you will experience the emotion of frustration regarding the Department of Veterans Affairs (DVA), however, you must never give up your faith in the United States of America.

The government system that I am referring to is The Department of Veteran Affairs, Disability Benefits and Pension Qualification System. The veterans who are requesting and applying for veteran benefits, because of emotional or physical ailments which occurred while he/she served in the military, are facing a long and demeaning process. I will explain in detail within the proceeding chapters of this book.

When entering the military each man and woman swore to defend this country. In return, they were promised certain benefits under the GI Bill and the use of the Veteran Administration Hospitals and all its service, etc. These benefits were to be provided to all veterans for a lifetime, depending on when you entered the military. This was not only a written contract but a verbal contract which should be binding by The United States Government. The veterans were, and are, willing to die for their country to meet their part of the contract. The key to receiving VA benefits is to earn any type of "Honorable Discharge."

All veterans upon entering the military are required to take an oath to the United States. This is the oath that the non-commissioned officer swears to:

"I, ____, do solemnly swear (or affirm) that I will support and defend the Constitution of the United States against all enemies, foreign and domestic; that I will bear true faith and allegiance to the same; and that I will obey the orders of the President of the United States and the orders of the officers appointed over me, according to regulations and the Uniform Code of Military Justice. <u>So, help me God</u>.

U.S. Armed Forces Code of Conduct

And in addition, the veteran has also sworn to uphold the U.S. Armed Forces Code of Conduct;

I

I am an American, fighting in the forces which guard my country and our way of life. I am prepared to give my life in their defense.

II

I will never surrender of my own free will. If in command, I will never surrender the members of my command while they still have the means to resist.

III

If I am captured I will continue to resist by all means available. I will make every effort to escape and to aid others to escape. I will accept neither parole nor special favors from the enemy.

IV

If I become a prisoner of war, I will keep faith with my fellow prisoners. I will give no information or take part in any action which might be harmful to my comrades. If I am senior, I will take command. If not, I will obey the lawful orders of those appointed over me and will back them up in every way.

V

When questioned, should I become a prisoner of war, I am required to give name, rank, service number, and date of birth. I will evade answering further questions to the utmost of my ability. I will make no oral or written statements disloyal to my country and its allies or harmful to their cause.

VI

I will never forget that I am an American, fighting for freedom, responsible for my actions, and dedicated to the principles which made my country free. I will trust my GOD and in the United States of America.[1]

PERSONAL VETERAN'S CODE OF
FIGHTING FOR DISABILITY BENEFITS

Truth shall spring out of the earth; and righteousness shall look down from heaven.
Psalms 85:11KJV

When the veterans are fighting for their rights, disability benefits, they should apply the U.S. Armed Forces Codes to their struggles, however, never lose respect for the country that has established a process to help the emotional and physical disabled veterans;

(I)
Know that I am again fighting for a way of life that has been promised to me by the United States Government.

(II)
Never surrender and do not allow myself to fall into a depression, remain proud.

(III)
If denied my benefits (and you will be) continue to fight by all of the means available, appeal.

(IV)
When I am denied, or when first filing a claim, I will keep faith with fellow veterans and join a veteran support group to help (DAV, VFW, etc.).

(V)
When questioned, (completing the application for benefits), do not evade any answer, give details and provide date, locations, units and any other information that is pertinent to my claim and only speak the truth.

(VI)
Never forget that I am an American fighting man or woman, fighting for my freedom, which in this case, are the benefits that you have already earned. And at no time forget, "I will trust my God and in the United States of America."

In 1966, I signed a contract with the United States of America to honorably serve in the military (U.S. Marine Corps). Before entering I was advised of my rights and the benefits that would be available to me while I served and after I was discharged, which included the GI Bill, housing, education, business loans and a life time of free medical assistance through the Veteran Administration Hospitals, and many other benefits.

We, the veterans, had no knowledge that over the years the contract(s) we signed would be changed by government mandate. Laws were passed to redefine our benefit package(s). For example, when I entered the military, military medical benefits were supposed to be free to all veterans. For care, we only needed to show we were honorably discharged. Recently, at a Veteran Administration Hospital, I was asked if I had a private insurance carrier and if I am a disabled veteran? At that time, I was not listed as a disabled veteran, so I had to pay co-payments through my insurance. However, disabled veterans are given the requested treatment as per their original contract, as they should.

Before you are granted your VA, disability benefits you will become very familiar with the Department of Veterans Affairs very specific requirements as to who can or cannot receive their benefits. You will learn how they make their decisions on your military background and their interpretation of the veteran's military medical records. You will further learn their terms regarding whether the veteran was operational and/or non-operational, and/or a combatant and non-combatant. The interpretation of these terms can cause the veteran an additional year or two years of research to prove why a non-operational, non-combatant veteran was serving in a hot combat zone and was possibly injured or suffered emotional problems. Basically, the veteran has the burden of proof of any injuries; emotional problems; his area of operation and, in many situations, the name of a veteran (with signed affidavit from that veteran) who can prove your statements as to combat action.

PERSONAL CASE EXAMPLE

Cast Thy burden upon the Lord and He shall sustain thee.
Psalms 55:22 KJV

This case example is being presented to the reader so she or he will have a complete understanding of the depth of the Department of Veterans Affairs (DVA) denial process, even when what appears to be a cut and dry case, it's not.

In many claims, the veteran will go through the grueling process of completing paperwork and obtain all necessary supportive documentation, including Military Medical records only to be denied his or her disability benefits. What does this mean? Basically, it means the claimant must start the process over. At this point most veterans become frustrated and do not appeal their claim.

Read the following case so you will understand that with perseverance, truth and faith you will win your battle, As I did.

Example: I was medevac'd from HUE' Province (Vietnam), during the TET OFFENSIVE in 1968 and spent 6 weeks in a mental hospital in Okinawa. However, before my rotation back to the U.S., I returned to my area of operation in Vietnam and completed my tour. Thirty-six years later, when applying for Post-Traumatic Stress Disorder (PTSD) and Diabetes Mellitus II disability benefits, I was denied disability benefits by the Department of Veterans Affairs on the grounds that they considered me to be non-operational and a non-combatant. I was told that only infantry is considered to be combatant. It became my responsibility to prove that I was stationed in this hot combat area, and that we took incoming (Artillery, Rockets, Mortars, etc.) before being considered for any disability benefits during an appeal process.

When my original claim for PTSD was forwarded to the DVA, I had already been interviewed by two Veteran Administration assigned Psychiatrists, both of whom diagnosed me with PTSD. Their reports were included with my claim. Even with this information, the DVA requested that the veteran, me, advise them of one specific action/event, date and location that caused the emotional problem and provide a witness, 36 years later.

The Department of Veterans Affairs, regarding diabetes, wanted the veteran (me) to prove Agent Orange was dropped in the soil on or near my area of operation. The government took over 10 years to admit to using the Agent Orange chemicals and the effects it had when dropped by US Military aircraft on our military troops who served in Vietnam. The medical problems with a copy of the DVA's decisions will be covered in proceeding chapters as will the issue of the Gulf War Syndrome.

Why am I covering these aforementioned examples? Because, **"Common sense is not so common when interfacing with the Department of Veteran Affairs."** Being medevac'd and having additional aliments (common to your combat area of operation), recorded in your military medical service record is insufficient proof to obtain disability status and or to be granted DVA disability benefits. Keep in mind, "us old guys" from Vietnam are from the "pre-computer era" and will have a challenging time in obtaining all our records. The easiest way to prove an in-service problem is through military medical records. The DVA will automatically attempt to compile your medical records when you file your claim. There may be a problem, some of the medical records have been lost or burned in the St. Louis Military Records Center fire, and some have been misplaced. In many cases, especially, those of the combat veterans, they may never have been a record created if you were injured while in the field.

For now, your burden of proof is demonstrating to the DVA that you were injured or have a psychological problem (emotional problem) while in uniform or specifically while in a combat area. With the DVA you need proof because they will not take your word for anything and, in some cases even when verified by military medical records. Basically, if you were in combat and not infantry they will request, in writing, that you explain why you, a non-grunt, were forced into a combat situation. It might be that the Department of Veterans Affairs has not yet learned that incoming does not check the MOS of the individuals on ground zero.

All of the veterans and their families who are entering a claim for disability benefits need know is to be prepared for the uphill battle. Maybe my experiences, written about in this book, will help relieve you of some frustrations and enable you to get your benefits in a more expedient manner. I have received my disability benefits from the Department of Veterans Affairs but not without a fight and prayer. Good luck, stay in your faith and God bless.

CHAPTER 2

How and where do I start?

God is our refuge and strength, a very present help in trouble.
Psalm 46:1 KJV

FILING FOR VETERAN'S DISABILITIES AND BENEFITS

I started with the knowledge that this will be at least a two or three-year process full of pitfalls and frustrations. Know that you need a survival kit which should consists of; (1) obtaining a Veteran Service Officer (VSO) or a District Service Officer (DSO) to direct you; (2) a strong home, family and outside (friends) support system; (3) have a strong will to overcome the obstacles which will be placed in your path, and (4) most of all, have faith in your almighty God. With this knowledge, you are now ready to embark on the road to obtaining your Veterans Disability Benefits.

Many veterans are completely unaware of a free resource that is available to assist them in getting the benefits they need and deserve. The resource is your Veteran's Service Office. Veteran Service Offices are normally located at VA Regional Offices and VA Hospitals and Clinics. These offices are not operated by VA employees but personnel from non-profit organization(s). They are run by one of many military veterans' service organizations such as the Veterans of Foreign Wars (VFW), Disabled American Veterans (DAV), AMVETS, etc. The counselors who work in these offices are referred to as either Veteran Service Officers (VSOs) or District Service Officers (DSOs), Veterans Counselor, etc. These counselors are often dedicated veterans who are committed to assisting you with the process of being enrolled in the DVA, filing claims, and pursuing your hard-earned benefits and compensation. These men and women are your friends who do care about you as a person. <u>It is of the utmost importance that you trust a VSO and/or DSO.</u> Their guidance will eventually get you through the process as rapidly as possible.

However, it is also important for the veteran to provide truthful and detailed information, in a timely manner, to the officers so they can act on your behalf. The only knowledge they have regarding your claim is what you present in your verbal interview and your written documentation. Take time to prepare your documentation, answers to all questions truthfully with very specific details and again, provide written proof wherever possible.

My first step was to contact many my friends who were disabled veterans. These men became my outside support group during this process and from this time forward. They personally knew of the organizations and of the individual personalities of the VSOs and DSO's. I was directed to an organization and a DSO who not only helped me but understood my fears of applying for disability benefits. Yes, fears! All of us veterans know that we did our job to the best of our ability. However, we will always have a little guilt for applying for disability benefits because we have seen our brother and sister veterans with a lot more serious injuries and emotional problems then we have. Don't let this pride stop you from your disability benefits. Go forward and know that you have earned the right to file your claim for DVA disability benefits.

In my case I went to my local VA Hospital Information Desk and asked to be directed to the veteran's organizations. I was directed to an adjoining building where all the organizations were in one area.

Veteran's Personal Notebook

And the Lord answered me, and said, write the vision, and make it plain upon tables, that he may run that readeth it.
Habakkuk 2:2 KJV

For the vision is yet for an appointed time, but at the end it shall speak and not lie: though it tarries, wait for it; because it will surely come, though it tarry.
Habakkuk 2:3 KJV

This notebook is not required; it is a tool to make your records keeping easier.

The veteran's personal notebook is the history of the veteran's military background. It shows how the evolution occurred and why a decision was made for the veteran to file a DVA disability claim. It also provides the foundation for support while going through the complex Department of Veterans Affairs process. This notebook provides credibility to the veteran's disability claim.

Failure to include all supportive information does a disservice to the Department of Veterans Affairs and yourself. It also does a disservice to the Board of Veterans Appeals (BVA), they need your information to review your medical and emotional status before awarding or disapproving compensation.

You need to build the notebook chronologically. Group the notebook by topic and importance of collected data, supporting your claims. When making a claim, always tell the truth and provide the supportive data regarding your claim.

PERSONAL NOTEBOOK DEVELOPMENT AND RECORDS

Planning the veteran's personal notebook centralizes information regarding past and present information supporting your disability claim with the Department of Veterans Affairs. This notebook is a tool to be used to assist you, and the DVA, to provide information which will allow the DVA a more time-efficient system in understanding and ascertaining your claim status.

Do not throw any DVA documentation, communication, medical information out. File everything appropriately, including duplicates of all letters you have sent to them.

The proper development of a notebook can serve as an "informative guide and records storage base" to be used while going through a frustrating and complex DVA process.

You need to arrange information chronologically, identify important persons, i.e. VA representatives, doctors, addresses, medical records, etc., and provide a snap shot of supporting information regarding your claim(s).

The major reason for creating and carrying this notebook to a meeting(s) (Department of Veterans Affairs Representatives and your personal service organization representative) is to assist in shaping your future by providing your DVA representative, members of your claim decision board and yourself with a better understanding of your physical and/or emotional disability claim(s).

THE NOTEBOOK AND INDEX TABS

(Purchase a notebook/binder, 3 ringed, 3 inches)
Index Tab One – (create your title)
A copy of your DD214.

The name, address and phone number of your DVA representative, etc.

Keep a list of your basic service-connected medical problems.

Include all important papers, i.e. marriage license, divorce certificate, children's birth certificates, social security papers, etc.

Extra DVA forms, i.e. authorization and consent to release information forms.

Index Two - VA claims applications

Requests and claims for service-connected compensation.

DVA form showing income, net worth and employment statement.

Index Three - Official VA responses and DVA decisions.

Index Four - Your letter(s) of disagreement and additional evidence to prove your claim.

Index Five – PTSD and DVA stressor letter, applicable only if applying for PTSD.

Index Six – Veteran's appeal letter(s).

Index Seven – Support data for your claim.

Index Eight – Make an index for anything pertinent to your claim, i.e. medical records and visits.

Index Nine – Include the following:

All signed return receipts and a description of the document sent.

Name of DVA person contacted by phone, the phone number and the reason for the call.

List all visits to the VA hospital, clinics, therapists, etc.

Maintain a medical history section listing all medical visits, including the doctor's names, addresses, dates, times, phone number and reason for the visit.

List all duty stations, locations and beginning and ending dates, along with your job classification.

THE US POSTAL SERVICE

The U.S. Postal Service is very important to your line of communication between you and the Department of Veterans Affairs. In many situations, a DVA Representative may not have received the documentation that you mailed to his office. The DVA is no different than any other corporation. It is run by people and people make mistakes.

The US Postal System, as well as UPS, FedEx, etc., has a registered mail and return receipt system. When the veteran sends mail to the DVA, the aforementioned systems should always be used. This will provide the veteran with the name of the person who received your mail, and the date and time received. This will also allow a system of tracking your documentation within the DVA. However, within your personal notebook you will establish an area of storage for these receipts so you can provide the VA representative with a copy of your documentation. Do not give-up this copy. You should be prepared to provide a copy of the necessary documentation to your representative on the spot.

THE DEPARTMENT OF VETERANS AFFAIRS REPRESENTATIVES

The first requirement of the Department of Veterans Affairs Representative is to determine if your claim is well documented with supported information regarding your physical and/or your emotional disabilities. A supported claim should consist of three elements:

The veteran must provide and produce medical evidence of a present disability, whether it is physical, mental or a combination of both. This information must be supported by medical records signed by a doctor(s) and or therapist.

The veteran must provide information that will establish that the physical and/or emotional disability was, or is, service-connected. This includes a variety of ailments such as disease, exposure to Agent Orange, Post Traumatic Stress Disorder (PTSD), Traumatic Brain Injury (TBI), Gulf War Syndrome (may not be completely recognized by the DVA), radiation, toxic chemicals, a verifiable stressor and others, combat and/or non-combat related injuries and disorders.

Next comes the required connection between the service-connect disability and your current disability. You should provide service medical records and prove medical relationship between the service-connected disability and your present disabilities.

CHAPTER 3

Appeals Section

(Anger) – For His anger endureth but a moment; in His favor is life: weeping may endure for a night, but joy cometh in the morning.
Psalms 30:5 KJV

(Depressed) – The Lord is nigh unto them that are of a broken heart; and saveth such as be of a contrite spirit.
Psalms34:1 8KJV

(Appeal) – Ask of Me, and I shall give thee the heathen for thine inheritance, and the uttermost parts of the earth for thy possession.
Psalms 2:8 KJV

The author of this book has been rated 100% disabled for his PTSD and physical injuries received while serving in Vietnam. He has personally experienced and lived through the following frustrating Department of Veterans Affairs (DVA) appeals process and is providing the reader with an advanced road map to navigate through the DVA process.

APPEALS: QUESTIONS YOU MAY ASK YOURSELF

(Always have a Veterans Service Officer working with and for you.)

The Board of Veterans' Appeals is part of the Department of Veterans Affairs, which is located in Washington, DC. Benefit claims are reviewed by members of the board and determinations are made by local DVA officers which issue decisions on appeals. The Board members, and attorneys who are experienced in veterans' law and in reviewing benefit claims, are the only ones who issue Board decisions.

Board of Veterans' Appeals

An appeal is a formal petition regarding your rights that needs to be written and filed for review by the DVA regarding your claim. You can request a review of a DVA determination on your claim for benefits issued by a local DVA office.

Filing an Appeal

Any veteran can appeal who has filed a claim for benefits with the DVA and has received a determination from a local DVA office. The veteran has up to one year from the date the local DVA office mails you its determination on your claim to file an appeal. After that, the determination is considered final and cannot be appealed unless it involved a clear and unmistakable error made by the DVA. I re-appealed on the fact that there had to be an error if I was denied, because all the evidence I presented was true and could be validated by my military Service and medical records. I filed my re-appeal and won my case.

Items you can Appeal to the Board

You may appeal any determination issued by a DVA regional office on a claim for benefits, which would also include eligibility for medical and emotional treatment such as PTSD and TBI. You may appeal a complete or partial denial of your claim or you may appeal the level of benefit granted.

ITEMS YOU CANNOT APPEAL TO THE BOARD

Not within the board's jurisdiction are decisions concerning the need for medical care or type of medical treatment needed, such as a physician's decision to prescribe or not to prescribe a particular drug(s), or order a specific type of treatment. Sometimes, the Board receives an appeal of the type but has no legal authority over this type of case, so it must be dismissed.

In my cases, there were no drugs prescribed, but in many cases VA counseling is ordered as a specific treatment. However, while I served in Vietnam, under combat conditions of the TET Offensive (1968), I was pulled from my duties and sent to a military mental hospital, out of country, for acute anxieties, today know as PTSD. I was in the mental hospital for 6 to 8 weeks and upon my request was sent back to Vietnam to finish my tour. Thirty-five years later I applied for my benefits for PTSD. The VA Psychiatrist at a Veteran's Administration Hospital, evaluated and diagnosed me to have PTSD. He wrote his positive findings in his report to the Department of Veterans Affairs, which stated that I presently suffered from PTSD. The DVA took it upon itself to re-evaluate his professional diagnoses and denied my claim regarding my suffering from Post Traumatic Stress Disorder. When you know you are being truthful and have medical documentation to back your conditions and or have been ordered to have a specific type of treatment, at a VA facility, accompanied with a Veteran's Administrations report(s), appeal and re-appeal the DVA negative findings and demand a clear reason why the DVA disagrees with the findings of the Doctors at the Veteran's Administration Hospital..

THE APPEAL PROCESS

All that is needed to begin the appeal process is a written statement indicating that you disagree with your local DVA office's claim determination and that you want to appeal it. This statement is known as a Notice of Disagreement which indicates why you disagree with the determination.

WHERE TO FILE YOUR APPEAL

With exception, you would file your appeal with the same local DVA office that issued the decision you are appealing, since that is where you claim file is located. However, if you have moved, file at your new location since that is where your claims file will now be being kept.

ITEMS TO BE INCLUDED IN YOUR APPEAL

If you feel that the decision made by the board was incorrect, it is important to send the DVA evidence that supports you that its determination is wrong. If you have additional evidence, submit the evidence to the office holding your claims folder.

If your file is still at the local DVA office send your new evidence there. You will receive a Supplemental Statement of the Case from the DVA. The new evidence will be placed in your claims folder and will be reviewed by the Board.

You always have a right to send new evidence to the Board for review without going through your local DVA. A written statement must accompany the new evidence stating that you waive a local DVA office review of the new evidence. Without the waiver, the Board will send your new evidence to your local DVA office. This action will cause a considerable delay in processing your new evidence and your claim.

RECOMMENDED COURSE OF ACTION:

(Always have a Veteran Service Officer (VSO) working with and for you.)

If you intend to appeal do the following:

- Work from the veteran's notebook that you put together as it makes finding your information easier.
- Always have an appeal representative assist you.
- File your Notice of Disagreement and VA Form 9 as soon as you decide you want to file an appeal to prevent a delay in your claim.

- Be as specific and detailed as possible when identifying the issues, or issues, you want the Board to review on your behalf.

- Be specific when identifying the sources of evidence, you want the DVA to obtain.

- Provide the DVA with full names and addresses of all physicians who treated you, and the date and purpose and/or treatment of the visits, Military and civilian. You will also need to provide a list of all injuries that occurred to you during military service and base national and foreign and copies of military medical records.

- Keep the DVA, and your VSO, informed of any personal change to your current address, phone number or number of dependents.

- Be aware that copies of your doctor's treatment records are generally more helpful than just a statement from the doctor.

- Always maintain a copy of every DVA and medical visit in your personal VA notebook.

- Be clear on your VA Form 9 about whether or not you want a Board of Veterans Appeals hearing and where you want it held.

- Talk to your VSO before requesting a hearing.

- Provide all the evidence you can that supports your claim, including additional evidence or information requested by the DVA for review before an appeals hearing.

- Always include your claim number on any correspondence you send to the DVA and have it ready if you call the DVA. This helps the DVA find your records.

ACTIONS, THE DON'TS:

Don't try to "go it alone". Get a VSO to assist you. A skilled representative can save you a lot of time.

Don't send in unnecessary documentation that doesn't have anything to do with your claim.

Don't use the VA Form 9 to start a new claim.

Don't use the VA Form 9 to request a local office hearing. Write to that office instead and request a return receipt from the post office for proof of delivery.

Don't raise additional issues for the Board late in the appeal process.

Don't submit a last minute request for a hearing or change of time.

This don'ts, will result in a delay in receiving a final decision regarding your appeal.

BOARD OF VETERANS APPEALS

The final decisions on any, and all, appeals are made by the Boards of Veterans Appeals. A claimant may be represented by a VSO agent or an attorney. The board also reviews fee agreements between appellants and attorneys or agents. Before hiring an attorney, review your rights regarding claimant's attorney fees and past due benefits, with your VSO.

BRIEF REVIEW OF THE APPEAL PROCESS

- If the recent disability compensation benefit awarded was not enough, you can appeal.
- If you have recently had problems with the DVA approving benefits for education, pensions, or any number of other benefits, you can contest that decision.
- Advise your VSO of your decision and ask for guidance.
- You have recourse through the DVA Appeals Process.
- Claimants for DVA benefits have the right to appeal decisions made by a DVA regional office or medical center and have one year from the date of the notification of a DVA decision to file an appeal.
- You may appeal a complete or partial denial of your claim or you may appeal the amount of the benefit granted and/or the level of your disability rating.
- Again, work with your VSO; ask for his or her guidance before

making any decisions to move forward regarding the appeal.

ELIGIBILITY

Any veteran or spouse who has filed a claim for disabilities benefits with the DVA and received a determination from a local DVA.

WHAT TO DO NEXT

Always have a VSO working with and for you. He/she is there to help you. Read more about the BVA and the US Court of Veterans Appeals. When you decide to go forward with an appeal read the following Appeals Process.

THE OVERVIEW- APPEALS SUMMARY PROCESS

(Always have a Veteran Service Officer working with and for you.)

Overview - Appeals Summary

1. To start the appeal process a claimant must file a written Notice of Disagreement with the local DVA or medical center that made the decision.

2. This is your written statement that you disagreed with your local DVA office's decision and you want to appeal.

3. Submit your notice of disagreement to the same local DVA office that issued the decision you are appealing.

4. If you have received a notice of determination be specific about which issue(s) you are appealing.

5. After receiving the notice of disagreement, the DVA will mail you a Statement of the Case describing what facts, laws and regulations were used in deciding your case.

6. If you wish to continue your appeal, you must complete and submit a VA Form 9 within the prescribed time.

7. It must be sent within the Statement of the Case, or within one year from the date the DVA mailed it decision, whichever is later. Contact your VSO and have him or her review the

form and the reason for your appeal.

8. On VA Form 9, clearly state the benefit you want and point out any mistakes you think the DVA has made in its decision.

9. Submit new information or evidence with your VA Form 9 to your local DVA office.

10. It is possible to get an extension for continuing your appeal you have to submit your VA Form 9 and write to your local DVA office handling your appeal and explain why you need extra time.

11. Once you have filed your appeal with your local DVA office, it will be forwarded to the Board of Veterans Appeals.

12. Your VA office will send you a letter when they receive your claims folder.

13. To eliminate the level of possible confusion, work with your lawyer and always check with your VSO or advise him of your intentions.

14. Until your file is transferred to the Board, your local DVA office is the best place to get information about your appeal. Your VSO should be able to assist you regarding your appeal.

15. The Board processes appeals files in the order received. It will assign your case a docket number. You may have to wait one or more years after you file your appeal for the Board pass a final decision on your case.

16. You have a right to a personal hearing. A personal hearing is a meeting between you and your legal representative, if you have one, and a DVA official who will decide your case.

17. A local office hearing is held at your local DVA office between you and a "hearing office" from the local office's staff.

18. To arrange a local office hearing, you should contact your local DVA office or your appeal representative while working through your VSO.

19. Be aware that a personal hearing may take some time to arrange. Most BVA hearings are held about three months before the case is actually reviewed by the Board.

20. The board will notify you when it receives your appeal from the local DVA office.

21. When a decision has been reached, the Board will notify you in writing. Your decision will be mailed to your home address, so it is important you keep the DVA informed of your current address.

22. If the claimant/you die(s) before the Board makes a final decision, the case is normally dismissed without a decision.

23. Survivors may file a claim at the local DVA office for any benefits to which they may be entitled. They can also as your VSO for assistance and direction.

24. The case keeps its original place on the Board's docket, so it will be reviewed soon after the Board receives it.

25. If you disagree with the Board's final ruling, appeal to the US Court of Veterans Appeals for Veterans Claims.

26. To get more information about the Notice of Appeal, methods for filing with the Court, Court filing fees and other related matters, you can as your VSO for information regarding US Court of Appeals for Veterans.

27. If you appeal to the Court, you should also file a copy of the Notice of Appeal with the VA General Counsel.

Always have a veteran service officer and/or an attorney working with and for you.

APPEALS POINTS OF UNDERSTANDING

The Board has been known to make mistakes. If you believe the Board made a mistake in its facts findings or in the laws that affected it decision in your case, you can file a written motion for reconsideration. Check with your VSO for guidance to determine if you should file for such a motion.

You can request that your case be re-opened if you have definitive new evidence. You will need to submit your new evidence directly to your local DVA office.

CHAPTER 4

State Politicians

REQUEST FOR HELP FROM YOUR STATE POLITICIANS

Then Festus, when he had conferred with the council,
Answered, Hath thou appealed unto Caesar? Unto
Caesar shalt thou go.
Acts 25:12 KJV

When a veteran is denied his or her appeal for disability benefits it is a normal procedure for the Department of Veterans Affairs to formally advise the veteran, in writing, of the appeal procedures available allowing him/her to disagree with its negative finding(s). The letter might also advise you to obtain an attorney to help you in your fight for the benefits that you have already earned.

When this happened to me, not only could I not afford the attorney fees, I did not want to give an attorney a percentage of a retroactive check when I won my case. Therefore, what I did was to create a package of my claim with all of my supportive data and a copy of all denial letters that I had received from the DVA. That package was made from the notebook that I had been creating throughout my experience. I had this documentation copied and bound at a local print shop on white paper but in a brightly colored folder. A bright package will not sit on an employee's desk for long because it stands out like a sore thumb. People will take notice of this unusual package.

I sent a copy of this package registered, return receipt requested, to two state Senators, two local Congressmen and the State Governor. I also sent copies to the DVA Board of Appeals and my DVA representative.

While the politicians cannot change a DVA finding, they can and will inquire into the decision. I used the system on itself and they became my free attorney, of sorts. It did work and I was given my disability benefits within 6 weeks. I had already fought my way through the DVA system for over 3 years and through 2 denials. I had to appeal and re-appeal. I did exactly what I described here. You will have to do the same thing with the help and guidance of your VSO. Don't give up because each denial is a step closer to you receiving those benefits that are due to you. You will also need the complete support of your spouse and your family. Your support system is invaluable because it is a port in a very long storm.

ACTUAL LETTERS SENT BY CHAPLAIN B. BOWMAN REQUESTING ASSISTANCE FROM HIS STATE POLITICIANS

(Do not copy this letter as your own. Your specific information is needed for your case to be evaluated.)

US Senator Barbara Boxer
Headquarters
501 "I" Street, Suite 7-600
Sacramento, CA 95814
(916) 448-2787 fax (916) 448-2563

CDVA Department

1227 "O" Street
Sacramento, CA 95814
1-800-952-5626

Note: This plea for help was also forwarded to: Governor A. Schwarzeneggar, Congressman Brad Sherman, Congressman Duncan Hunter, and Senator Dianne Fienstein. These were the political powers in California at the time this book was written, 1ˢᵗ edition.

Date: _____

RE: Your Name and VA file number

I sincerely need your help. I need to share with you a very frustrating experience that is unfortunately, not mine alone. This is a request for assistance (help). I am a Vietnam War Veteran who served with the 3ʳᵈ Marine Division in a combat zone. I received combat pay while in Vietnam from approximately October 1967 thru November 1968. I need your help in reviewing my military files to ascertain and prove that I was, in fact, in a combat situation while in Vietnam and eligible for my disability and/or pension benefits.

I am being denied all disability benefits and or pension because my military job description (MOS- #) Job title _____, did not qualify me, to be considered for my earned disability benefits. While in Vietnam, I volunteered to escort on truck convoys and river boats gear on the river which included tons of ammo on the boat. I have been denied because as a Marine, near the DMZ in 1967-1968, "TET Offensive", I was not considered to be in a COMBAT SITUATION by the Department of Veterans Affairs in July 2003. However, I was under enemy fire, rockets, mortars, booby traps, artillery and small arms fire on numerous occasions and received combat pay from the US Government (military) while I served in Vietnam.

I have also attached to this package a DVD of me in a combat situation near the DMZ. It was filmed in Sept. 1968 at Cua Viet Fire Support Base at the mouth of the river, approximately 4 miles from the DMZ. This super8 film, which was transferred to DVD, includes pictures of me on a mike boat that took a rocket hit, and at least 10 additional boats were hit and burning in the background. Four American Military men were killed during the attack. The DVD has been sent to each of my DVA Representative, at the

Department of Veteran Affairs (prior to their decision) and to the Disabled American Veterans Organizations, with my appeal.

It has been over a year since I filed an appeal regarding the Department of Veterans Affairs decision to deny all of my requested disabilities and VA disability benefits. Because of the time period (length of time, again, over a year) of the appeal, and no apparent decision(s), I have compiled all of the pertinent information and documents (copies of my requests, denial letter(s), medical evaluations and a copy of the aforementioned DVD and DVD written narrative, explaining the DVD minute-by-minute, etc.) to be sent to your office and a number of additional leading and respected politicians in the State of California.

I was also denied all requests for my Veteran Disabilities Benefits by the Department of Veterans Affairs, even though the Veteran Administration Doctors and Veteran Administration Psychiatrists, in 2003, confirmed my physical and emotional injuries and the fact that I do have Post Traumatic Stress Disorder (PTSD) which occurred while I was in Vietnam in a combat area – Phu Bai, near and in Hue City. When checking my military records (Vietnam), the Department of Veterans Affairs, determined that I was medevac'd to a mental hospital in Okinawa, after diagnosis by Military Doctors at two hospitals in Vietnam, for "Multiple episodes of chronic anxiety", today known as PTSD. I was a patient at the mental hospital for weeks and went through therapy sessions (I can't recall how long) then I went back to my original assignment in Vietnam, escort duties on river boats near the DMZ. I re-volunteered to go back to Vietnam and to be placed on the small river boats, again in harm's way because I'm a Marine. At a later date I was again, injured and hospitalized in Vietnam, I did complete my full tour.

Sign_____**date** _____

Name of veteran: _____**VA File number:**_____

Address: _____, Home phone _____,

Fax _____, and email address

SSN #__ Military Service ID number# ____, Date of Birth: ___
Place of Birth: _____, Married to _____
    Branch of Service – _____, (2) Honorable Discharges,
Highest rank – _____ MOS: _____, Length of time in the service
– (example, <u>Jan. 1966</u> Thru <u>Jan. 1972</u>)
    Length of time in Vietnam – [example, <u>Oct. 1967</u> thru <u>Nov. 1968</u>
(3rd Marine Division)]

THE COMBAT ACTION RIBBON

I was told by DVA Representatives, if I would have been awarded the "Combat Action Ribbon", (CAR), I would have had **"No"** problems obtaining, at least, my request for PTSD benefits. Mr. _____, VA National Service Officer, Los Angeles Office has helped me a great deal. He provided me with a computer print out regarding the CAR that stated;

"The Combat Action Ribbon – This award was created by the Secretary of the Navy (Note [SECNAVNOTE] 1650 of 17 February 1969". I was discharged in Nov. 1968 and had no knowledge that the CAR was issued or of its importance to obtaining benefits that I earned while in combat. *__The Ribbon did not exist when I was honorably discharged from the military.__* **Prior to this "CAR Ribbon" being issued, combat pay status was additional proof that I was in the combat arena.** It seems that the requirements changed after I was discharged; however, my fighting a war did not change. It happened.

RIBBON REQUEST AT THE DIRECTION OF THE DVA:

Department of Veterans Affairs
Columbia
1801 assembly Street
Columbia, S.C. 29201

National Personnel Records Center (314) 801-0800
Request # _____ Social Security Number, _____

US Marine Corps, Navy Personnel Command Center
(901) 874-3350 (901) 874-5111 DSN 882-5111

DD215 Corrections Department (901) _____,
Mr. _____
Mr. _____ (same phone), received both request for my DD214 update.
(Excellent man to work with, very helpful)

In Feb. 2004 and April 2004, I requested that my DD214 be updated to show a "Combat Action Ribbon." This would be accomplished on the updated DD215. On Oct. 2004, I checked on the status of this request, I was informed, by the two agencies/organizations listed, that because of the backlog" The National Personnel Records Center and the Navy Personnel Command Center (US Marine Corps)", would possibly get to my request, in another 3 to 4 months. I'm going forward with my request for DVA disability benefits in accordance to the government policies. According to the government polices this information is supposed to be provided to the veteran within a 20 to 26-week period and the appeal to have a decision within a year. (I have not received the requested ribbons as of this date.)

(Note: Each veteran must research his area of assignment and his military unit. It can help give him or her supportive data from DOD records. A search should provide you with needed information).

Further DOD records will show that in 1968, from the fire bases at Cua Viet to Dong Ha and along the shore and on the Cua Viet River approximately 213 American Military were killed and approx. 746 American Military were wounded. During the same period of time approx. 1,270 enemies were killed, wounded unknown in the same locations. This was my escort area of responsibility in 1968. I consider that the aforementioned information and my military records, including medical records, will prove that I have been in a combat situation (Department of Defense records information).

Again, I sincerely need your help. This process is a very frustrating experience that is adding undo stress to me and my family. This is a request for assistance (help).

Thank you,

Full name and signature

Name of veteran: _____ **VA File number:** _____

Address: _____, Home phone _____, Fax _____, and email address

SSN #__ Military Service ID number# ____, Date of Birth: ___ Place of Birth: _____, Married to _____

Branch of Service – _____, (2) Honorable Discharges, Highest rank – _____ MOS: _____, Length of time in the service – (example, Jan. 1966 Thru Jan. 1972)

Length of time in Vietnam – [example, Oct. 1967 thru Nov. 1968 (3rd Marine Division)]

The aforementioned example letters can be used as a hard copy, with "**only your information**" provided to whom you consider you're political/DOD champion(s) in these matters.

PERSONAL CASE AUTHORIZATION FORM (EXAMPLE)

(An important fact: Without a personal letter of authorization or a Department of Veterans Affairs government form of authorization, the DAV cannot obtain information on the behalf of the veteran.)

Name of veteran: _____ **VA File number:** _____

Address: _____

Home phone _____, Fax _____, and email address

SSN # _____ Military Service ID number# _____

Date of Birth: ____ Place of Birth: _____

Divorced from 1st wife, _____

presently married to _____

Branch of Service – _____

(2) Honorable Discharges, Highest rank – _____

MOS: _____

Length of time in the service – (example, <u>Jan. 1966</u> Thru <u>Jan. 1972</u>)

Length of time in Vietnam – [example, <u>Oct. 1967</u> thru <u>Nov. 1968</u> (3rd Marine Division)]

Federal Agency Involved: Department of Veterans Affairs, California Department of Veterans Affairs, Disabled American Veterans, National Personnel Records Center, Navy Personnel Command Center (US Marine Corps), additional needed information VA File # _____ and Personnel Records Request ID# _____.

Assistance being requested: This is a request for assistance (help). I am a Vietnam War Veteran who served with the 3rd Marine Division in a combat zone (I received combat pay while in Vietnam) from approximately October 1967 thru November 1968. I need your help in reviewing my military files to ascertain and prove that I was, in fact, in a combat situation while in Vietnam and eligible for my disability and pension benefits.

It has been over a year since I filed an appeal regarding the Department of Veteran Affairs decision to deny all of my requested disabilities and VA disability benefits. Because of the time period of the appeal, and no apparent decision(s), I am asking for help.

I authorize any US Governor, US Congressman, US Senator and/or their delegated staff to inquire on my behalf regarding my case and to receive information relating to it.

Signature _____

Date_____

(Example for the State of California)

A request for assistance in obtaining Veteran Disability Benefits was sent to the following representatives <u>for the State of California</u>;

Governor Arnold Schwarzenegger
134 Hall of the States   State Capitol Bldg
444 North Capitol Street NW   Sacramento, CA 95814
Washington D.C. 20001   (916) 445-2841 fax (916) 445-4633
(202) 624-5279 fax (202) 624-5280

US Congressman Brad Sherman
1030 Longworth Bldg.   5000 Van Nuys Blvd, Suite 420
Washington D.C., 20515-0524 Sherman Oaks, CA 91403
(202) 225-5911 fax (202) 225-5879
(818) 501-9200 fax (818) 501-1554

US Congressman Duncan Hunter
2265 Rayburn House Office Bldg. 366 South Pierce Street
Washington D.C., 20515   El Cajon, CA 92020-4136
(202) 225-5672 fax (202) 225-0235
(619) 579-3001 fax (619) 579-2251

US Senator Dianne Fienstein   Angela Kung, Caseworker
Representative
11111 Santa Monica Blvd, Suite 915   One Post Street, Suite
2450
Los Angeles, CA 90025   San Francisco, CA 94104
(310) 914-7300   (415) 393-0707

US Senator Barbara Boxer   CDVA Department
Headquarters
501 "I" Street, Suite 7-600   1227 "O" Street
Sacramento, CA 95814   Sacramento, CA 95814
(916) 448-2787 fax (916) 448-2563   1-800-952-5626

The aforementioned example letters can be used as a hard copy, with your information provided to whom you consider your champion in these matters in your state.

Research is needed to obtain the politicians information in "your state."

CHAPTER 5

Medical Issues (physical and emotional)

(The Veteran Administration Hospital and VSO will assist you in locating an approved counselor and or psychologist when dealing with your emotional concerns. Always have a Veteran Service Officer (VSO) working with and for you.)

O Lord, rebuke me not in thine anger, neither chasten me in thy hot displeasure.

Have mercy upon me, O Lord; for I am weak: O Lord, heal me; for my bones are vexed.

My soul is also sore vexed: but thou, O Lord, how long?

Return, O Lord, deliver my soul: oh save me for thy mercies' sake.

For in death there is no remembrance of thee: in the grave who shall give me the thanks?

I am weary with my groaning; all the night, make I my bed to swim; I water my couch with my tears.

Mine eye is consumed because of grief; it waxeth old because of all mine enemies.

Depart from me, all ye workers of iniquity; for the Lord hath heard the voice of my weeping.

The Lord hath heard my supplication; the Lord will receive my prayer.
Psalms 6:1–9 KJV

Before reading this chapter, it is important for the reader to understand when I am referring to physical and emotional issues it is from my own life experiences.

I am aware that there are a number of conflicting psychological schools of therapy and theories directed by professional with the following disciplines: social workers, priests, rabbis, chaplains, psychologists, psychiatrists, physicians, and family and friends who will provide you with immediate advice and guidance. I am not pretending to know or understand these specific psychological disciplines. However, I am saying that you should go to your local VA hospital and ask for help from the proper professional who has an understanding of your specific problem, or disorder. That person will be assigned to you.

I will briefly cover psychological disciplines and treatments used by the VA professional. I do not consider myself to be an expert in treating warriors and/or civilians with psychological problems.

PTSD, can be defined as an anxiety disorders caused by trauma, an emotional wound caused by a range of traumatic or stressful events. It's normal for warriors and or civilians to react to an abnormal event or situation (war) which the individual has no immediate control over, such as individual field combat experience and attacks.

Trauma can take many forms, from the most disturbing circumstances such as witnessing death in combat or any other violent event (injury, divorce, auto accident, psychological and/or physical abuse, rape, etc.) that you may have been exposed to while serving in the military. Any person, a combatant and/or a non-combatant can be affected in their emotional state. Anxiety occurs when the brain perceives a threat. It sets off a chain of physical changes that prepare the body for flight or fight.

It is important for the veteran to know that he or she may have a Post Traumatic Stress Disorder and or a Traumatic Brain Injury and again, it may not surface until your senior years, especially the retirement years, 55 and up, your golden years. The Veterans Administration Hospital will test you upon request.

And be not conformed to this world, but be ye transformed by the renewing of your mind, that ye may prove what is that good, and acceptable and perfect will of God. Romans 12:2 KJV

The following are two nursery rhymes which can be used to define the plight of the emotionally injured soldier and the emotionally injured soldier's family and or spouse.

Let's take a good look at my military versions of well-known nursery rhymes, because this is what you and I have been living with.

MR. DUMPHREY

Mr. Dumphrey sat on a wall,
Sgt. Dumphrey had a big fall,
All the President's men (Doctors, medics and therapist),
Couldn't put Sgt. Dumphrey together again.

Mr. Dumphrey sat on a wall

The wall is a place of rest, a place of introspection, a place to make life changing decisions.
All military personnel have sat on that wall and made the choice to join the military.

They understood that they might go to war which added great weight to their final decision.

Psychologically speaking, while on that wall you will also have to deal with many new emotions.

When you join the military, you will climb many additional walls regarding career changes, family, breaking emotional ties with your civilian life and dealing with the treat of going to war.

Sgt. Dumphrey had a big fall,

- Sgt. Dumphrey went to war and returned with deep emotional wounds, known as PTSD
- Others returned with invisible physical wounds known as TBI
- Many warriors who fell have physical and emotional wounds.

All the president's men, (Doctors, medics, and therapists),

- The battlefield responders, corpsmen and field hospitals are the warriors responsible for saving the lives of the soldiers in the field.
- Warriors who have been seriously physically wounded are treated on the spot and sent to a rear hospital in a partially safe zone to save their lives.
- Warriors who have been traumatized by the events they witnessed have developed emotional wounds, such as combat stress, acute anxieties, shell shock, fear, etc., while still in the field. These men and women should be immediately evaluated and diagnosed with a serious emotional problem.

Couldn't put Sgt. Dumphrey together again.

- Many male and female warriors may never be diagnosed with PTSD when discharged from military service. However, a signal to a possible disorder will come from family and friends. In some cases, they will tell the returning warrior that they are different and that they are not the same person they knew. The warrior will never again be a completed civilian.

- The warrior diagnosed with PTSD and/or TBI may receive treatment while on active duty in the military. Upon discharge, the warrior is advised to seek assistance form the DVA and the VA hospital.

- The veteran, now a civilian, will go through a number of DVA and VA paper processes which will add to his/her PTSD through frustration.

- A veteran must know that they can live a productive, healthy life with PTSD, which is a permanent disorder.

- It is possible to become violent, homeless and or suicidal with psychological help.

- The author of this book as a returning warrior had to learn to deal with PTSD.

ANNE AND BILL

Anne and Bill went up the hill,
To further her career growth,
Sgt. Anne fell down, and broke her psyche,
And Bill came tumbling after.

Anne and Bill went up the hill,

- The hill is a place of family discussion, a place of martial introspection, a place to make life's changing decisions, enter the military or not.

To further her career growth,

- Anne joined the military for pride, a career and educational benefits

- Anne wanted to better her life and family status, a life with a future.

Sgt. Anne fell down, and broke her psyche,

- Sgt. Anne went to war
- Sgt. Anne came home with PTSD
- Civilian Anne could not get help from the Veterans Administration Hospital and or Dept. of Veterans Affairs
- Anne was told that he had a chemical brain imbalance
- Anne felt helpless
- Many warriors come home with a personality change, which indicates PTSD. Families and friends cannot understand or deal with the warriors changes: rage, mood swings, withdrawal, etc. In Anne's case, after time, she was divorced.

And Bill came tumbling after

- Many veterans come home and because of their personality change (PTSD) the wife, family members and friends tend to stay away from the veteran.
- The husband, Bill did not understand what his wife was going through, an emotional disorder.
- Bill tumbled; he divorced Anne to search for a new life.
- In some cases, at this point, Anne may become homeless or commit suicide or in the positive, she may search for psychological help provided by the Department of Veterans Affairs.

TBI AND PTSD

There is no complete cure for either Post Traumatic Stress Disorder (PTSD) or Traumatic Brain Injury (TBI). There are effective treatments being discovered and implemented at military facilities across the nation, programs such as Warrior Mind Training, a mental focus and mind training for Soldiers, Sailors and Marines.

Both civilians and military personnel must understand that between two to five percent of the nation deals with some form of mental illness. In many cases we are not always aware of our mental disorders.

It is also apparent that the Department of Veterans Affairs, when faced with a combat applicant filing for disability due to PTSD, denies the applicant and advises him/her that he/she possibly has a chemical imbalance of the brain and not PTSD. The emotional disorder becomes personal and not related to a traumatic event in a war zone, then not listed as service-connected. This is a very heavy stigma placed on the veteran and his/her family because the family is unaware of the traumatic events that their loved one had experienced. With the denial from the DVA to provide assistance, it places a stigma on the truthfulness of the returning warrior and can divide him or her from their family support unit. This can cause the warrior frustration and send him/her deeper into their PTSD disorder.

It is imperative that the veteran be aware of some of the symptoms of chronic emotional disorders. At least one of the aforementioned symptoms will appear when the veteran is under stress.

The following is a list of some, but not all, of the symptoms related to emotional disorders that the veteran might experience:

- Fear and/or paranoia.
- Violence and/or rage.
- Confused thinking and a fear of learning.
- Bizarre behavior.
- Impaired judgment.
- Lack of contact with reality, deficient coping skills.
- Cannot commit, difficulty with relationships.
- Sleeping disorders, flashbacks
- Drug abuse, alcohol abuse.
- Spousal and/or child abuse.
- Lack of motivation.
- Vulnerability to stress, see PTSD triggers.

SOME DANGER SIGNS OF PTSD

PTSD occurs when someone experiences or witnesses a life-threatening traumatic event and has a short or long term reaction. In most cases, it is the prolonged reaction that affects the soldier. Throughout this book, many PTSD symptoms that have been covered may not be recognized as being in direct connection with a traumatic event.

ALCOHOLISM

A dependence on alcohol, which is marked by the repeated excessive use of alcoholic beverages, may indicate PTSD. The development of withdrawal symptoms if you reduce or cease its use can be an indicator. Other markers can include cirrhosis of the liver and a decreased ability to function socially and vocationally.

ANXIETY

Anxiety is marked by a distress or uneasiness of mind which can be caused by fear of danger or misfortune, as well as a state of apprehension and psychic tension.

BORDERLINE PERSONALITY DISORDER (BPD) CAN BE CONFUSED WITH PTSD

BPD is marked by a confused way of thinking a confused way of thinking, poorly regulated emotions, an overwhelming desire to control other people, sexual domination over a partner, no compassion for the feelings of others, impulsivity, impaired perception and reasoning and markedly disturbed relationships.

DEPRESSION

Depression is marked by as condition of general emotional dejection and withdrawal; sadness which is greater and more prolonged than is reasonable.

PTSD AND THE FAMILY

When a man or woman joins the military, they are aware that they will be sent to a duty station anyplace in the world, including a war zone.

Their families also understand that, for four or more years, their loved one will be home for only a short period of time during their military leave(s).

While a serviceman is serving, especially in a war zone, the family, wife, children, mother father, etc., pray for his or her safety. They pray for a safe trip home and an honorable military discharge bringing their loved one back to civilian life. The family shows complete support while he or she is in the military.

However, upon their return, in many cases, the family faces a person with a completely different personality. The personality change is usually caused by Post Traumatic Stress Disorder (PTSD). The family members should make every effort to understand their returnee and not expect him or her to be the same person who left. It may take months or years for the PTSD to surface.

When it finally happens, and it will, many families withdraw and either cannot or will not understand the changes. This is when the family support is needed the most. However, the family and the returnee have not been educated about the symptoms of PTSD and/or that it is an emotional disorder that can lead to suicide, homelessness, unemployment, violent beatings and, in some cases, murder.

I am introducing the families to a few symptoms and triggers of PTSD in the hopes that it will help them understand the depth and seriousness of this disorder.

Symptoms:

A symptom is defined as an indication of a disorder (PTSD) or disease which, when experienced by an individual, bring about a change from a normal function, sensation or appearance. These are some symptoms of PTSD:

- Repetitive speech, meaning that the veterans will repeat things that have already been said
- Distressing thoughts
- Numbness
- Out of touch with your feelings
- Detachment from family, friends, former military buddies.
- Sleeping disorders, including difficulty sleeping or inability to fall asleep.
- Difficulty concentrating.
- Outbursts of rage.
- Anger, frequently uncontrolled and/or despair.
- Hyper vigilance
- Depression and anxiety.
- Unusual personal bedroom habits. Some veterans lay their clothes next to their bed, like a fireman. In some cases, they must keep a weapon close to their bed. They own a dog(s) as a warning system and are always ready for action.
- Insomnia
- Nightmares
- Hidden thoughts of killing or injuring a person.
- Many become loners who cannot commit to a relationship, cannot hold a job, cannot work dressed in a uniform or carry a gun.
- Unseen fears; upset, uptight and prone to panic attacks, out-of-control emotions.
- Defensive and/or frustrated, violent, feelings of hopelessness and discouragement.
- Prone to addictions involving sex, alcohol, drugs and tobacco.
- Unusual and/or self-destructive behavior, (attempted) suicide.
- Guilt, family disruption, sexual dysfunction.
- Homelessness and lack of trust.

- Child and spousal abuse.
- Problems handling stress.
- Flashbacks
- Mood swings, headaches, shame over taking someone's life in war.
- Loss of spiritual and religious faith.
- Lack of self-esteem

PTSD TRIGGERS

Triggers are often harmless cues that have become associated with the original trauma relating to a traumatic military event. Many triggers can activate traumatic memories and stimulate intrusions, causing us to recall the unwanted memories.

When you are in the military you expect to be in violent situations and/or to be made aware of possible violence against you as an individual. A good example of being exposed to violent situations starts in military boot camp where war is always on your mind. In the Marine Corps, we were trained in combat technique and instructed to yell, Kill," as we went through are moves.

When you are discharged from the military, in most cases, you will never face the same types of violent events presented to you in the military combat. It is very possible that activities you enjoyed prior to the military, such as hunting, paintball sports, camping, skydiving, and target shooting and watching different types of movies can act as a PTSD trigger that will affect the veteran for life.

When you are going through a major personality change, you need to find a therapist. Go to your local Veteran Administration Hospital and Department of Veterans Affairs for assistance. The therapist is aware of the causes and effects of PTSD.

PTSD Triggers:

A trigger is defined as a point that, when irritated or stimulated, will give rise to physiological or pathological change.

It is important that veterans find it helpful to understand PTSD triggers by some of their categories:

- Visual: - seeing blood in a butcher shop or auto accidents with injured persons animal road kill, plane crash, violent movies, black garbage bags reminds a veteran of body bags, etc.
- Sound: - Holiday marching band, a backfiring car sounds, a gunshot, the sound of track vehicles, low flying aircraft or helicopter, etc.
- Smell: - smells of smoke, smells of gun powder, the smell of dirt and/or overgrown areas, smells of the jungle bring, dirty clothing will bring back memories of war.
- Taste: - the metallic taste of cheap silverware, canteens, field rations, beer cans, etc.
- Physical or body: - kinesthetic means the sensation of movement, tension or body position. Thus, running or jogging when tense brings back memories of running from incoming shelling, etc.
- Tactile or touch: - pressure around wrists or waist (POW), being gripped, held or restrained, reminds the veteran of hand-to-hand combat, torture, etc.
- Pain: - the pains of war are numerous and have meaning to each individual, whether emotional or physical.

The following are some triggers of PTSD related to me by individuals who has experienced combat:

- Reliving the event which could include bad memories, flashbacks and negative dreams or nightmares.
- Disinterest in activities which, at one time, gave pleasure, such as: camping, hunting, sports shooting, parachuting, scuba

diving, hiking, road trips (reminder of convoys), group sport activity, flying, boating, water sports, social parties (crowds), etc.

- Dark clouds, rain, mud, because, in Vietnam, soldiers were wet, living and walking in mud and were attacked on dark cloudy days because there was no American air support.

- Thunder and lightning. Thunder reminds the soldier of artillery fire and/or incoming explosions. Lightening reminds the soldier of when artillery is fired and is accompanied with a bright flash.

- Grief brings back a flood of negative recall and emotions.

- Movies that are bloody, violent, stressful or war movies.

- Crowded movie theater/church, etc. I personally have to sit on an aisle seat for fear of a possible emergency (incoming). I cannot run to safety from the middle of the row.

- Pain, for obvious reasons.

- Sandy beaches

- Loud sounds and blasts on such occasions as the Fourth of July, Memorial Day, military parades, sound of track vehicles.

- Video games, such as war games when you have to kill to win. If you have a child they will want to own home video games, etc., and will want Daddy to play. Most family members will not be able to understand why you cannot play.

- Barking dogs because, in Vietnam, dogs would hear the incoming artillery rounds before any human could. When they would bark and run towards a bunker, you would also run.

- Do not like or accept authority figures. You become a perfectionist at work to avoid stress from management; cannot deal with micro-management or direct orders.

- Spiders, snakes and insects.

- Camping.

- Touch, a person does not want to be physically touched.

- Demonstrators. The Vietnam veteran was not accepted in the

United States when they came home. In some situations, men re-enlisted to stay in their comfort zone rather than return to the US. To this day, Vietnam veterans are still put down by many US citizens.

- Visual images, negative thoughts, smells that bring back memories, identity issues and self-esteem issues, sounds, memories, certain tastes, false memories.
- Divorce, which is a major stressor.
- Auto accident(s), which is a violent action.
- Subway tunnels and trains.
- Popcorn popping.
- These are some, but not all, possible triggers for the veteran. You might be experiencing others that are not listed.

Every military person who has PTSD will have a number of the aforementioned triggers and symptoms. However, each individual also has his/her own triggers and symptoms and will deal, or not deal, with his PTSD in his or her own way.

It is important a person obtain medical and psychological help from the Veterans Administration Hospital or a medical facility within their area.

WHO AM I?

Repeat after me: "I am a returning warrior who has honorably served my country". It is important to also look at yourself and acknowledge yourself before looking at the depth of your physical or emotional wounds. What you think of yourself should be used as a point of reference when you ascertain who you are. Do not allow your traumatic experience to take away your self-esteem. It should be noted that not all military traumas are caused by war. A non-combatant can also experience trauma while in the military.

TRAUMATIC BRAIN INJURY (TBI)

Traumatic Brain Injury can be caused by a serious bodily injury or shock, as caused by a blast. Violence in combat and/or witnessing a disturbing event with lasting psychological or emotional impairment can cause Post Traumatic Stress Disorder (PTSD).

TBI is caused by any near explosion, violent jolt (which can occur in an automobile accident), a hard hit while playing football, a blow to the head (such as a hard fall to the ground striking your head), a violent shaking or a penetration to the head, which results in a head injury that is followed by a temporary, or prolonged, loss of a function of the brain, as in a concussion. A concussion is a form of TBI, however, not all violent shaking or blows to the head result in TBI. A veteran can have a head injury or a brain injury that does not cause functional changes affecting thinking, body movement, bodily sensations, language and/or emotions which are some symptoms which are indicative of TBI.

TBI, PTSD and concussions are related, they all are associated with severe multiple trauma, emotional and/or physical trauma.

GULF WAR SYNDROME (GWS) OR ILLNESS (GWI)

The US government has not officially accepted Gulf War Syndrome or Illness as a recognized disorder caused by the Gulf War. However, veterans who served in the first Gulf War, known as Desert Storm, have complained of symptoms that they attribute to GWS. Some symptoms include fatigue, nausea, indigestion, depression, headaches, cancer and bodily pains, to name a few.

As a Gulf War veteran pursues his or her battle with the DVA, he/she must remember what happened to the Vietnam veteran regarding issues of chemical warfare. The Vietnam veterans were told, by the US government, that there were no chemicals used that would affect the US soldiers and, for approximately 15 years, the government denied its use of Agent Orange in Vietnam.

When the US soldiers were home and dying for years, well after the war, the government still would not acknowledge Agent Orange and its devastating effects. Eventually, the US government did admit it dumped the Agent Orange chemical on its troops. The conclusion is that the men and women of the Gulf War should unite and continue to fight for their disability benefits regarding the chemicals used in the Gulf War by either side involved in the conflict. You must fight for the rights you earned and understand that the government will wait for many to die, then admit to the effects on the soldiers of the Gulf War and pay the few who hung in there for the fight.

AGENT ORANGE

Agent Orange is a toxic herbicide sprayed by the US government/military during the Vietnam War to defoliate jungle areas and expose the enemy force, it proved to be deadly to combatants on both sides. While the government denied for years they had sprayed this toxic chemical, the effects of it were undeniable. The following was explained to me by a member of the Veteran Administration Hospital during my personal medical examination.

The following is a short list of service connected health problems directly related to Agent Orange. I personally have interviewed many veterans with these aliments:

- Chloracne - a skin disease.
- Myeloma – a cancer of the blood cells.
- Non-hodgkin's lymphoma – a skin disease with liver defects.
- Porphyria cutanea tarda – a skin disease with liver defects.
- Respiratory cancers of the lung, larynx, bronchus and trachea.
- Soft tissue sarcoma of the muscles and tendons.
- Prostate cancer.
- Chronic lymphocyte leukemia.
- Adult onset Type 2 diabetes.

It took the US government from January 1965, to July 1993, before making its initial report which led to presumptive service connection for several health problems among veterans. It is unknown how many veterans died before the government finally took responsibility for its actions and acknowledged <u>their diseases</u>.

In the wars of today, all veterans must make every effort to obtain their disability benefits through the DVA. If you, as a Vietnam veteran, have any of the aforementioned health problems, go to the VA hospital and request to be checked for these diseases caused by Agent Orange. The DVA and the VA hospital are there to help you.

STRESS

Briefly stated, stress is the rate of all the wear and tear caused by everyday life. Stress during war and individual combat situations has its own deep effect on the warrior's emotional and physical well-being. Stress is not always something bad, it can be a warning system to rest, and a body can shut down. In my case, during the Vietnam era while under heavy stress, in a combat situation I lost my speech, for approximately two weeks. It can also be an invigorating experience for another person. Examples of such invigorating experiences might include jumping out of a plane, surfing large waves, skiing higher slopes, auto racing, etc. We have all experienced similar stressful but invigorating situations because those are the things which bring excitement to our lives.

PROBLEMATIC STRESS

Negative stress can be caused by a number of events, such as:

- Busy highways or freeways, heavy traffic.
- Long lines at airports, delays.
- Micro-management, work related stress.
- Low income with numerous bills.
- Health problems and no insurance.
- Family stressors and negative relationships.

- War, not in your control.
- Deaths of comrades, family, etc.
- Political issues that affect the country

Every person handles stress differently. Many military personnel and civilians as well consider a number of these stressful events as traumatic. Some will be affected by a traumatic event for a short or long period of time, depending on the circumstances of the event and the nature of the person who experienced and perceived the event. PTSD can be debilitating after the effect of the stressful traumatic event has occurred. This reaction to a traumatic event, especially if it is war related, is normal.

MILITARY AND COMBAT STRESS

The effects of the military and war on a young person will last a lifetime. Military life, in and of itself, is stressful. In most cases you leave home, mom and her loving self with her lovingly prepared meals. The first day in boot camp, there is no love, just a loud voice yelling at you and giving you orders to perform immediate physical exercise and eat quick meals in the mess hall. Your world and your life have just been converted from a peaceful existence to a world of organized chaos, stress, war, injury and possible death.

I have mentioned military and combat stress to inform all veterans, military combatants and non-combatants as well, that they can be affected by traumatic events caused by the military. If you are a non-combatant, do not let the DVA base your traumatic experiences on war only. There have been recruits accidentally killed and injured in boot camp and advanced training. You are an individual and the events you have lived through and/or witnessed are yours as well. How you handle a traumatic event is also personal. If you need professional help then push the DVA until they provide you with the benefits you earned. When you joined the military and swore the oath, you stated that you were willing to die for this country. The DVA must acknowledge you and assist you in your time of need.

This list of stressors can affect anyone, combatant or not, however relating to the military:

- Emotional numbness starting from boot camp.
- Helplessness from joining the military and questioning yourself if you did the right thing.
- Fear regarding if you may die or become an amputee in a combat situation.
- Tension, which becomes on-going.
- Difficulty sleeping.
- Racing heartbeats from stress form boot camp, combat or because you are in the military.
- Shock over life being converted from civilian to military.
- Worry over if you go to war, who will take care of your immediate family?
- Anger towards some drill instructor, authority figure.
- Grief because your life as a civilian has died, and will never be the same.

In many cases, you have been emotionally wounded and you will have to learn to live with it, however you must always request help

from a therapist.

CHAPTER 6

Can a Veteran get help for emotional problems?

And thine ears shall hear a word behind thee, saying, this is the way, walk ye in it, when ye turn to the right hand and when ye turn to the left. I saiah 30:21 KJV

"Ask and it will be given to you; seek and you will find; knock and the door will be opened to you." Matthew 7:7 KJV

"For God did not give us a spirit of timidity, but a spirit of power, of love and of self-discipline." 2 Timothy 1:7 KJV

The Veteran's Administration Hospital and the Department of Veterans Affairs can and will direct veterans to professional counselors, therapist, psychotherapist and psychiatrist.

Many psychiatrists and psychotherapist believe cognitive therapy can help the veteran. It was developed as a structured, short-termed present oriented psychotherapy for depression which can occur in all aspects of life for professional persons, civilian and military. It was developed to assist in solving immediate problems by modifying unwanted, dysfunctional thinking and behavior. It is a psychotherapy system developed to incorporate and/or unite theory of personality and psychopathology supported by factual empirical evidence.

Cognitive therapy and other therapy programs focuses on change in the following behaviors; automatic thoughts, behaviors, protective rules, and core beliefs.

Automatic Thoughts- When an unwanted, distorted, possible harmful automatic thought goes unchecked, it strengthens your dysfunctional core beliefs by adding another unwanted memory to the schema, and it changes your thought belief. However, if that unwanted dysfunctional thought can be altered, by a non- dysfunctional automatic thought, this process will assist the warrior/client via thought, and causing a dispute between two opposing memories, it will minimize the effects by changing the core structure.

Conditional Beliefs - An attempt is made to help the veteran identify conditional rules and find flexible healthy alternatives. The psychotherapist will then test them by using cognitive disputation and empirical research.

Protective rule - Veterans are encouraged to review evidence which supports healthier core beliefs frequently, by exposing one self to healthy behavior which counters unwanted, dysfunctional behaviors. This process should not be done or attempted without the guidance of a professional counselors, therapist, psychotherapist or psychiatrist.

Core Belief - Core beliefs are our realities. They are not as easily altered as automatic thoughts. Cognitive and other therapy will focus a great deal on your core beliefs.

SUICIDE

When a veteran feels he or she can't deal with life go directly to your family support group, a professional counselor, therapist, psychotherapist, psychiatrist, your Chaplain, Priest, Rabbi, friend and or to the Veteran's Administration Hospital, explain and ask for immediate help. You can receive help and prevent a needless death; you owe it to yourself to live.

An important area not reported enough, regarding active military personnel and veterans, is the rate of suicide which has occurred and is occurring.

The Vietnam era soldier came home to a very hostile United States. Many of today's top executives were demonstrators against the war in Vietnam and, even more unconscionable, the returning Vietnam veteran as individuals. The Vietnam veteran has never known peace in this country, the country that he was, and is, willing to die for in a combat situation. There are 58,000+ names on the Vietnam Memorial in Washington, DC to honor and praise these men and women.

However, what is not mentioned is that the Vietnam veterans who came home were treated so badly by the American public that over 110,000 of them have committed suicide. The government seems to have difficulty awarding a combat veteran a disability rating for PTSD. In many cases, the Department of Veterans Affairs (DVA) will advise the veteran that he or she possibly has a chemical imbalance in their brain, not PTSD. This frustration has triggered the PTSD and caused the veteran to feel helpless and in some cases, commit suicide.

The suicide figures repeated here are not new. Men and women who have served in all of our wars have experienced PTSD but under different names, such as shell shock, combat fatigue, acute anxieties et al. The government is aware of the psychological problems caused by war.

The Iraqi and Afghani wars are no different. A great number of returning veterans are experiencing the same frustrations. Since the start of these wars, there has been about 1 suicide every 2 ½ days. The veteran needs a strong support team, made up of family and friends, so he or she can live a productive life I society.

In today's military, especially the US Marine Corps and the US Army, the suicide rate has risen in suicides per year for the men and women who have served and are now serving within a combat zone.

Remember, help is available!

TRAUMATIC BRAIN INJURY (TBI)

TBI and PTSD have a definite relationship: Traumatic Brain Injury can be caused by a serious bodily injury or shock, as caused by a blast. Violence in combat and/or witnessing a disturbing event with lasting psychological or emotional impairment can also cause Post Traumatic Stress Disorder (PTSD).

TBI is caused by any near explosion, violent jolt (which can occur in an automobile accident, playing football, etc.), a blow to the head (such as a hard fall to the ground striking your head), a violent shaking or a penetration to the head, which results in a head injury that is followed by a temporary, or prolonged, loss of function of the brain, as in a concussion. A concussion is a form of TBI, however, not all violent shaking or blows to the head result in TBI. A veteran can have a head injury or a brain injury that does not cause functional changes affecting thinking, body movement, bodily sensations, language and/ or emotions which are some symptoms which are indicative of TBI.

TBI, PTSD and Concussions are related in that they all are associated with severe multiple trauma, emotional and/or physical.

HOMELESSNESS

So far in this book, Post Traumatic Stress Disorder (PTSD) symptoms and triggers have been discussed. The lack of support for PTSD from family and friends can lead to depression, etc. that, in some cases, will drive a veteran to suicide or homelessness, two places of escape.

Every day, we see the homeless in the parks, on the street corners or in mission lines for food, but we need to understand that all of these people started with self-esteem, pride, a home and someone who loved them. Many of the homeless are persons with PTSD caused by individual stressors and/or traumatic events such as war, divorce, rape, victims of a crime, economic depression, etc.

It is important that people understand the causes and effects of PTSD. The professional understands that there are treatments which can help the person in need. If a person can understand their triggers and communicate their problems or feelings with their support group, they may prevent the two daily sins of PTSD, suicide and homelessness.

VETERAN'S BIOLOGICAL NEEDS

A veteran's basic biological needs are: shelter, food, water, sleep, oxygen and, in some cases, companionship, or a support system, (military and civilian). An important need, which is easily forgotten or associated with the aforementioned needs, is psychological stability and a peace of mind. Without the above mentioned needs it is possible that the (returning) veteran will become suicidal or homeless.

IMPORTANT BIOLOGICAL NEEDS

Important biological needs include:

1. A balanced diet, rest and exercise. This can be difficult to achieve if you are stationed in a combat zone.

2. Positive verbal communication with your support team and/or family members.

3. Understanding that PTSD can interfere with your biological needs for relaxation and psychological stability.

4. Not allowing alcohol, caffeine, drugs or pill dependency to become a biological need. Many in the military, especially in the combat arena become addicted to what can be thought of as an aid to your relaxation. That is wrong and you will need to seek professional assistance to re-direct your needs back to the basics.

5. Monitoring and understanding your basic needs by paying

attention to your positive and negative symptoms being caused by PTSD. This is a biological need to protect you from unwanted negatives in your life.

6. Being able to identify physical, mental and emotional problems as they emerge. In many cases the warrior was not aware of his/her psychological problem until the military therapist informed them of their disorder.

7. Being able to identify persons, family members and friends, who are bringing negatives into your life, will help to clean you up and move towards positive people.

8. Always work with and trust the professional who are providing you with positive care, medication and treatment. The Veteran's Administration will provide you with best of care.

SOCIAL NEEDS

Social needs include:

1. "Survival skills" needed for a positive life is required for you to have a peaceful existence in areas such as; school, employment, communication, commitments, health and goal setting (short and long termed), etc.

2. Daily living skills, social communications, social awareness, money management, understanding your family and employment politics.

3. A person must know that there is a higher power, have faith and know that faith is positive and will get you through all of your problems but do not eliminate professional treatment and/or assistance.

PSYCHOLOGICAL NEEDS

A person, especially a veteran, needs a sense of wholeness, accomplishment, belonging, shelter and the required needs to remain alive such as oxygen, water, food, sleep, and faith in something or someone besides yourself.

When a man or woman is actively serving in the military, they have personal pride, high self-esteem and a sense of accomplishment. In many situations, this can be lost in a week, a month or years after discharge from the military. During this period of time it is important to have a strong support team which has an awareness of PTSD.

Understanding your psychological needs is the first step in the healing process.

Psychological needs include:

1. Developing a close alliance with a support team or individual who is willing to always be there with and for you.

2. Being a productive and useful to others and remaining active.

3. Finding a hobby, skill or job that you enjoy will assist in providing you with a positive balance and helping you to remain in a positive frame of mind.

4. Learning to relax and establish a place with a relaxed atmosphere. I relax by watching old Looney Tune cartoons, which offers me a mental and emotional place of safety.

5. Developing a regular daily routine that you can be comfortable with as a life style.

6. Understanding PTSD while knowing you are a strong person and you can turn negative memories into positive memories. You are in charge.

7. Seeking professional assistance and an additional support team if you have an addiction to alcohol, drugs, food or an abusive personality.

CHAPTER 7

DEALING WITH CLINICAL PSYCHOLOGICAL DISORDERS AND PROBLEMATIC STRESS RESPONSES

(The Veteran Administration Hospital and your VSO will assist you in locating an approved counselor and/or psychologist when dealing with your emotional concerns. Always have a Veteran Service Officer (VSO) working with and for you.)

Yet men are born to trouble, as the sparks fly upward. But as for me, I would seek God. And to God I would commit my cause – who does great things and unsearchable, marvelous thing without number. Job 5:7-9

My only advantage, as a veteran who has been diagnosed with PTSD and is daily combating its effects, is the realization that it is here and will be for the rest of my life so I have to learn to deal with it.

Over the years of self-exploration and research, I have had a thought which I often referred to in my time of emotional need.

That thought was "Denial is inexcusable and provides a deceptive and short-lived relief while hastening a long-termed emotional disorder". An important issue to healing that was never presented to me while I was undergoing therapy was the importance of God. You have to have faith in something or someone besides yourself. You have to have faith in God. It is important to always remember that God doesn't want the negatives in our past to control our present and/or future. When we ask Him for help, He will assist us in our time of need. In many situations, He will fight our wars and we will receive the victory. Have faith in God and believe in yourself. God is your companion.

COMBATING DAILY ATTACKS OF PTSD

It is definitely possible to combat daily attacks of psychological disorders by applying the following tasks and skills:

1. Think only positive thoughts about yourself and learn to accept and love yourself.

2. Live a God oriented positive life and remain optimistic and focused on going forward with constructive activities.

3. Socialize in military and civilian life and establish meaningful positive relationships.

4. Think of love and happiness and enjoy life.

5. Listen to others and acknowledge their accomplishments and be sincere.

6. When under emotional attack, let your support group, family and religious leader know. They are there to help you in your time of need.

7. Know when you are at a low emotional point you have to immediately focus on a better time.

8. Know that you cannot think of two things at the same time. When a negative thought enters your mind replace it with a positive one.

9. If you think of talking yourself into a positive mood, you are

already in the positive.

10. In life, you must establish reachable goals and, as you reach them, re-establish new ones. You are developing new positive behaviors.

11. Surround yourself with positive people.

12. Remove negative thoughts and negative people from your mind and your life.

13. Participate in any positive activity to combat your emotional fears.

It is important for returning combatants with PTSD to keep their lives in balance and do things to keep them physically fit, nourished and rested. It is also important to include pleasurable and satisfying activities in their lives. They need to be kind to themselves because they will feel that they are less than perfect when things don't go as smoothly as they would like. They also have to remember that help is available whenever they need it. Cognitive therapy and other psychological programs are effective in treating both religious and non-religious clients. There are many benefits to using psychological techniques in Christian counseling. Always keep your faith in God's hands.

Note: I am a Christian Chaplain and Counselor. However, a person will need to search their own religious and/or spiritual self while using, or being introduced to, cognitive techniques or other psychological programs.

Cognitive therapy techniques are suitable for a variety of people, but Christian clients are particularly well suited for this method. There are at least two reasons for this. One is that cognitive therapy requires clients/warriors to compare their thoughts with truth to see if they are understanding reality accurately. Coming from a war environment, this transition to civilian life can be difficult. This therapy is also challenging for agnostics who have difficulty finding standards for truth. Christians believe truth is revealed in Scripture, giving them a useful way to evaluate their thoughts and rid themselves of guilt.

The other reason that this method is well suited to Christians is that they believe in God's love, which is the only love that is purely unconditional. Many clients/warriors find their fears to be family rejection, abandonment or lack of love. Flawed human relationships with family or peers may have produced deep insecurities and fears. Treating those fears requires rejecting the core belief statement "My family does not understand me. I was more comfortable in war".

Those beliefs can be easily disputed by people who acknowledge God's unconditional love. Human relationships occasionally result in rejection, even by those closest to us, especially when a warrior returns and is no longer the innocent kid who went to war. God's love never results in rejection.

I have learned that we all have two fathers, a biological father and the Almighty Father. The biological father can let you down which might include possible rejection, but the Almighty Father will never let you down. However, when a warrior has a positive family support system, psychological assistance and a belief in God, he or she will be able to transcend their challenges and enter back into society in a productive manner.

At this point, there are two important issues should be discussed, and those are the issues of the Male and Female Stress Syndromes. Both men and women can be active in combat situations but will be affected differently.

MALE STRESS SYNDROME

1. Body Concerns, which might include, but not be limited to, sexual dysfunctions, headaches, fatigue, nausea, confused thinking, depression, etc.
2. Family concerns, debts to deal with upon returning from combat, family health issues, re-establishing conjugal relationships with your spouse, etc.
3. Career concerns, thoughts about what the combat warrior will do upon being discharged from the military. If a person

has PTSD they may never want to carry a gun or wear a uniform again, which rules out police careers. Many cannot go to medical school because they cannot deal with blood. The careers many young combatants dreamed of have been eliminated because of their PTSD. A warrior may come home with physical disabilities and, because of those injuries, will have to re-direct their career goals. If a warrior is married this may cause family complications.

4. Personal concerns, education, marriage, starting a family, career deadlines, income, working in a competitive world are some concerns a young warrior has to deal with while in the military. Many men elect to stay in the military and allow the military to care for them and their families.

5. Spiritual concerns, military men are trained for war, to hurt or kill others while following the orders of the government. To hurt or kill others can be going against a man's religious and/or spiritual beliefs. This can cause guilt which is a very powerful stress syndrome and can, depending on the individual, lead to depression.

FEMALE STRESS SYNDROME

The Bible recognizes men and women as God's creations who were created as equals. Over the years, the US Military has changed its regulations towards women in war. Women are not only allowed in war zones but they play a very important part of contributing to the war effort, equal to the men. Since the Vietnam era, the US has placed the military women on and over the battlefield.

The aforementioned Male Stress Syndrome is also directly related to our women warriors. However, women are also at risk for less well-understood stress symptoms stemming from their particular physiology, life changes and the social and psychological demands placed upon them in civilian and military life. Most of these stresses are long-termed and beyond their control.

Additional stress symptoms for women in the military include:

1. Menstrual tensions.
2. Pre-menstrual headaches, mood swings, cramps and general pain.
3. Post-partum depression.
4. Pregnancy and childbirth.
5. Menopause melancholia.
6. Frigidity and infertility.
7. Virginities are inflammation of the vagina.
8. Lack of orgasm which might be caused by painful intercourse.
9. Eating disorders, which may include anorexia, bulimia.

SERIOUS MENTAL AND EMOTIONAL DISORDERS AFFECTING THE MILITARY FAMILY

The military population is not only made up of the sworn military personnel, but also of their spouses, their families and their significant others. While the combatants are assigned away from home, all the family, work and financial responsibilities fall on the spouse. She or he also have the responsibilities of worry, not knowing the combatants situation, and the fears if their loved ones will return physically or emotionally disabled or, even worse, that they will not return at all, having been killed in action.

Do not think the sworn military personnel are alone with PTSD and other emotional problems. All stresses in this book can affect the families through no fault of their own. There are fears, depression, loneliness and they may have a deeper need for a strong support system that provides a basic understanding of what they are going through. They are as much a part of the military as the sworn personnel.

SYMPTOMS OF CHRONIC/SERIOUS MENTAL ILLNESS:

Acute, "positive" symptoms (at least one of these usually present, at least during an exacerbation of illness):
- Distorted perceptions; loss of contact with reality, caused by trauma of war.
- Delusions.

- Hallucinations.
- Disordered, disorganized and confused thinking.
- Unstable and inappropriate emotions.
- Bizarre behavior; impaired judgment.

Residual "negative" or deficit symptoms (several of these usually present most of the time):
- Vulnerability to certain kinds of stress.
- Extreme dependency (sometimes combined with hostility).
- Difficulty with interpersonal relationships.
- Deficient coping skills.
- Poor transfer of learning; fear of new situations.
- Restricted emotional response and lack of enjoyment.
- Reduced speech and impaired abstract thinking.
- Reduced ability to pay attention; slowness.
- Apathy; lack of motivation; phobic avoidance of situations.
- Sensitivity to over-and-under stimulation.

(Rule out depression, demoralization, social breakdown syndrome, medication side effects, or alcohol/drug abuse).

"NORMAL" REACTIONS TO SERIOUS ILLNESS:

These reactions are common in anyone who realizes they have a serious, chronic (incurable) illness, and may progress through stages (like the mourning process). Some of these characteristics are often present and can be misdiagnosed as positive or negative symptoms.

1. General stress response ("fight, flight, fright").
2. Grief; denial and impatience (lack of acceptance).
3. Anger and striking out.
4. Guilt and self-blame.
5. Depression; hopeless, helpless feelings; demoralization.

6. Regression to earlier levels of functioning.

7. Preoccupation with "self" (apparent disinterest in others).

8. Interruption of normal development (immaturity).

SOCIAL BREAKDOWN SYNDROME:

This includes loss of normal role functioning and varying degrees of extrusion (or exclusion) from normal family/community functioning. Characteristics are similar to the negative symptoms and also resemble institutionalization syndrome. Social breakdown syndrome can be a side effect of any treatment that removes the client/patient from his/her usual social environment or excuses him from usual role expectations (e.g., prolonged hospitalization or too much "overprotection" on the part of clinical staff and/or family members). In many cases of the veteran returning from war, there is a social breakdown while assimilating back into a family life.

COPING AND ADAPTATION

In many cases, warriors returning from a combat zone will have a social breakdown and have difficult time assimilation back into society and/or his or her family life. All too often, the warrior veteran will learn that they suffer from Post-Traumatic Stress Disorder (PTSD), Traumatic Brain Injury (TBI) or one or more of many other types of physical and/or emotional problems.

The combat veteran can learn how to cope and adapt with society and his newly discovered disorder(s). As he becomes aware of the problems he should immediately seek professional help. This help will provide knowledge of his disorder and how to cope with it to more successfully adapt back into society. The professional will also prescribe treatment, rehabilitation and, in many cases, assist the veteran's family in understanding the seriousness of his disorder. This will give you, the combat veteran, hope and directions in self-help.

As a returning combat veteran, you need to understand the following which can accelerate your rehabilitation:

1. You must not be in denial regarding your disorder and/or your physical disability.

2. Be curious regarding your illness and its treatment and rehabilitation.

3. Accept your situation and make every effort to be productive to society and your family.

4. Accept the therapy and remain an active participant with your doctors regarding treatment and rehabilitation.

5. Know you will need to modify your lifestyle so set realistic goals and expectations.

6. Keep your family aware of your treatment and your progress and your goals.

7. Your family is your support team and will offer love and security, if you allow them to do so. Invite them to take an active part in your rehabilitation.

8. Have faith that you will be able to have full participation in (your) life.

TYPES OF TREATMENTS AND REHABILITATION

You have been reading on how to cope and adapt to your new physical and/or emotional situation many times throughout this book. You have read the words treatments and rehabilitation. The professional who is assisting you will determine the type of treatments you will need to receive. Listen to him and follow his/her instructions. When these instructions are followed the rehabilitation will slow in a more expedient manner.

Here are a few general treatment conditions:
- Trust your doctor(s) who are knowledgeable and there to help you.

- Know you may have individual treatments, and individual and/or group rehabilitation, depending on your situation.

- Treatment may be provided by a number of medical

professionals and therapists so develop a positive attitude as you are being transitioned from programs and treatment components.

- If, as a solider, you were wounded in a combat zone, you will have many teams of professional assisting you from hospital to hospital. Accept that fact and understand there is a continuity of care.

- Part of your treatment is patient education regarding your wounds, emotional trauma(s), illness and the care and procedures which is being given.

- The military will always provide you with the safest and most comfortable surroundings as possible for your treatments and rehabilitation.

- Your treatment may start on the battlefield but, be assured, that your complete rehabilitation will be stateside depending on the seriousness of you situation.

- Understand that, depending on your circumstances, your treatment may be short or long termed. You will need to accept that to heal faster. It will become a way of life if you will let it.

- Here are a few rehabilitation conditions:

- Self-acceptance of your illness or disorder is imperative.

- You must be willing to accept the rehabilitation program prepared just for you.

- Involve your family in your rehabilitation.

- Stay away from self-pity.

- Approach your disability with a positive attitude and the strength of a warrior.

- Develop a realistic approach recognizing all phases and stages of your recovery. The doctor will explain all steps which you will go through to reach that recovery point.

- If your treatments have all been I a military hospital, know you will be going back into the civilian world and some people may reject you for the honorable work you did as a soldier.

- Depending on the seriousness of your injuries and emotional problems, you may have to deal with social stigma and family stigma but **DO NOT** belittle yourself with self-stigmatization.

- If you have lived through a traumatic event your group and family therapist can assist you. Work through your grief, guilt and the flashbacks. Attempt to replace your negative memories with positive memories.

- If you are religious or spiritual, have faith that you will once again become a productive part of society and that through your experiences you will one day be able to help others.

- General treatment and rehabilitation can be described. Each individual will be cared for by a professional who will prescribe the individual treatment and rehabilitation. I can only write what was taught to me during my rehabilitation as a Vietnam combat veteran.

- Maintain a good attitude.

- The doctors are your friends.

- You are going home to live out your life.

- Your family loves you.

- Most importantly, always love yourself and stay in faith.

NORMAL REACTIONS TO TRAUMATIC EVENTS AND/ OR COMBAT WOUNDS

With all of the aforementioned provided on treatments and rehabilitation, you will have a normal reaction to your serious situation. It is only human to react when you realize you have been wounded, have an illness or that you have lived through a traumatic event. To this day, I remember being in a military truck in Vietnam, being physically in the air then coming to in a military hospital. Know there are stages you will progress through to understand "the how and the why" that this has happened to you. You will experience the following:

- Fear.

- Where am I, especially if you were in combat?

- What happened to me?

- How did I get here, and how long have I been here?
- How serious are my injuries?

The answer to the aforementioned questions is standard and goes like this: "The doctor will be here to explain everything." During this period of time, you need to understand that you may go through a number of negative symptoms, such as:

Flashbacks to the event, a partial, but negative, memory.
Depending on the seriousness of the injury, you may go into denial and self-pity.

- Anger.
- Depression, feeling hopeless, helpless and fear of the future.
- Suicide can enter your thoughts.
- General stress or you may need meds to go to sleep.
- Self-grief due to lack of acceptance.
- Guilt, what did I do to cause this?
- You might become a loner, disinterested in others, including the family support team.
- Regression to how you recall civilian life and how you will fit into society.

REFINING THE MIND

The following two programs Warrior Mind Training and Vets Back to the War Zone have been established to help the combat veteran to become a productive member of society replace negative memories with positives memories and develop an inner peace. Members of both of these programs have met and are aware that we are working toward the same goals.

WARRIOR MIND TRAINING PROGRAM (PTSD AND TBI)

Warrior Mind Training is about sharpening and refining the mind to allow our men and women in uniform to achieve their fullest potential as warriors. Upon returning from war, Warrior Mind Training teaches members how to leave the battle on the battlefield; to reintegrate with self, family and society, and to earn the peace for which they have so honorably paid the price.

The bottom line is that all returning veterans need assistance in re-integrating with their families and society while maintaining their own inner peace. There are many VA programs and national associations that can provide assistance regarding PTSD and TBI. Contact the DVA, Veteran Centers, and/or your local Veteran's Administrative Hospital for more information about these programs.

WARRIOR MIND TRAINING AND OTHER ORGANIZATIONS PROVIDE HELP AT THESE LOCATIONS:

1. Fort Bragg, North Carolina
2. Warrior Transition Unit, Naval Medical Center, San Diego, California.
3. US Marine Corps Bases:
4. Camp Lejeune, North Carolina
5. Camp Pendleton, California
6. Air Station, Miramar, California

US Navy:

1. Amphibious Base, Coronado/North Island, California
2. Submarine Base, New London/Groton, Connecticut

Returning Combat Veterans

1. Veterans Center, Veterans Village of San Diego, California

VETS BACK TO WAR ZONE (VBTWZ)

VBTWZ is a non-profit organization, established to support veterans who are having problems being reintroduced back into society. It was formed to bridge the gaps between, healing the pains of war, stabilizing the veterans' emotions, working with veterans with Post Traumatic Stress Disorder (PTSD) by returning veterans to the source of their traumatic emotional event(s).

Its purpose is to return war veterans, at no expense, to the places they served during their time of war for therapeutic benefits related to Post Traumatic Stress Disorder (PTSD) and other psychological disorders.

Our goals are to provide the veteran with an opportunity to begin a therapeutic process to bridge the gap and root out the pain of war for these discontented warriors who may well have embedded problems and debilitating diseases. Many combat veterans have not had the opportunity to reconcile with the trauma experienced during battle, or to rid themselves of the demons they struggle with on a daily basis. VBTWZ will provide closure for love ones of those that made the ultimate sacrifice.

How is this accomplished? "Vets back to war zone" will work in partnership and/or joint venture with Professional Veteran Centers Counselors (VCC) throughout the Southern California area. They will be provided with a number of veteran volunteers who have PTSD and are being counseled by the VCC in their existing PTSD program. These veterans have been pre-evaluated as to their emotional stability and their willingness to travel to Vietnam and other war zones when safe, for emotional closure and a healing process.

A pre-trip interview will also be used to extract personal histories/ testimonials (memories positive and negative) from participating returning veterans. A post-trip interview will be conducted to obtain reflections of how the veteran sees their country of conflict and its people today. This information will be obtained by the Vets Back to War Zone, "Veterans' Oral History Committee." This will meet with the requirement established by the 106th Congress which enacted the "Veterans' Oral History Project Act" 27 October 2000.

How does all of this relate to applying for disability benefits with the Department of Veteran Affairs?

You are a warrior. Remember you are experiencing a normal reaction to your traumatic event and/or serious illness. It is a difficult process to recall the feeling you first had during the realization of your circumstances.

You are a warrior and you fought your way through the process. If you are reading this book, **YOU ARE A WINNER!** You are moving forward with life and you are taking the next step to possibly another battlefield. This battlefield is full of frustrations, obstacles, red tape, mines and mental games. It is called applying for your disability benefits through the Department of Veterans Affairs, DVA. You are a warrior and you have been through the worst scenario. Do not let the DVA frustrate you to the point of walking away from what you have earned, on many levels. You have been taught to fight for what you believe in, fight for security for yourself and your family. Do not forget what you have been through to get to the point of applying for your veteran's disability benefits.

CHAPTER 8

Chaplaincy and Counseling

HISTORY OF CHAPLAINCY

The Continental Congress recognized a need for chaplains and formed the first professional chaplains group in the Continental Army on July 25, 1775. This date established military chaplaincy to be older than the United States.

CHRISTIAN COUNSELING

Chaplaincy is a ministry reaching well beyond the structure of the traditional church. Chaplaincy is often accepted by those outside the church body, Military, Prisons and Hospitals because chaplains go where the church cannot, the battlefields. Chaplains do not preach denominationalism; they spread the healing word about the Kingdom of God allowing His word to flow through to persons in need.

Being a Vietnam combat veteran I learned there are no atheists in a fox hole. When the incoming rockets fall near your position the soldiers outgoing prayers become plentiful asking for survival and protection. When a chaplain assists a person regarding their needs, they never challenge a person's faith or advise them that their chosen faith is wrong. They will never reject a person because of his faith or absence of faith.

In most cases the chaplain has also been trained as a spiritual counselor with an understanding of methods of therapy. I will refer to a Christian Counselor only, even though, in the military, in many geographical areas, the serviceman will only have the chaplain to counsel him or her.

SERVANT'S ATTITUDE

a chaplain must be tactful, courteous and considerate in approaching all people regardless of race, sex, creed, faith, community and/or religion. Having a servant's attitude, as Christ did, is needed in ministry. A chaplain is a servant not only to the people of God, but to all at their place of ministry including battlefields.

Chaplains are professionals committed to reducing military stress, helping servicemen deal with personal and family emotional issues, easing potential violence and conflict in the on the base or in a combat location, with a focus on bringing improvement to a person's life. The key is to provide servicemen with a resource so they don't have to go it alone in challenging times. Chaplain's help Officers deal with the delicate personal situations within their unit(s).

CHRISTIAN COUNSELING RELATED TO THERAPY

(The Veteran Administration Hospital and VSO will assist you in locating an approved counselor and/or psychologist when dealing with your emotional concerns. Always have a Veteran Service Officer (VSO) working with and for you.)
But let him ask in faith, with no doubting, for he who doubts Is like a wave of the sea driven and tossed by the wind. James1:6

This chapter is dedicated to explaining chaplaincy and professional Christian counseling to the veterans who want to interface with a chaplain and a Christian counselor as his or her therapist.

Any form of successful counseling requires a healing atmosphere that generates hope and growth. This is difficult on the battlefield however the Chaplain does offer a calming effect to the soldier. During peace, the soldier often comes for "Christian counseling", not knowing there are many different guiding assumptions and techniques used by counselors.

Most Christian counselors agree that Christian counseling is not a matter of using scripture or prayer as a complete answer to emotional problems, however it will give the warrior an inner calm. The counselors know warrior's emotional problems are not necessarily spiritual problems. Their position is supported by many who study the integration of psychology and Christianity. To assume the warrior's spiritual health must come before emotional health denies that physiological, social and psychological factors contribute to emotional problems, both are needed.

Christian counselors recognize the overlap between spiritual and emotional health. They also help their clients/veterans experience both emotional and spiritual well-being by using a variety of spiritual disciplines and psychological techniques.

Christian counselors can enrich the serviceman's opportunities by blending excellent counseling with sensitivity to religious values and spiritual awareness. They also incorporate the disciplines of cognitive therapy which is based on the cognitive model, which hypothesizes that people's emotions and behaviors are influenced by their perception of events. Post-traumatic stress disorder is caused by traumatic events in a soldier's life.

Many Christian ministers and priests, when counseling clients, sometimes forget to use scriptures as a tool to assist in bringing the client out of his/her wilderness. Most of the veterans who are having emotional problems are coming from a place of wilderness, a war. We, as Christian and biblical counselors, have a responsibility of re-enforcing the ministers, priests and chaplains who are only using secular/clinical treatment methods, and bring them back to the methodology of Jesus Christ's teaching and healing, where accepted by the serviceman.

Why am I saying this in this book? It is to inform the veteran that he/she must be aware of the type of counseling that he wants to receive and by whom. He or she may request a secular and/or religious counselor that is best suited for him or her as an individual. However, cognitive therapy has been effective in treating religious clients and there are many benefits of using cognitive techniques in Christian counseling.

The sovereign Lord has given me an instructed tongue, to know the word that sustains the weary. He wakens me morning by morning, wakens my ear to listn like one being taught. (Isaiah 50:4)

BIBLICAL COUNSELING:

A Christian/Biblical counselor and/or therapist is a specialist in counseling through the biblical word and secular clinical counseling. Those brought up knowing the Bible and it scriptures will be comforted by their faith as they go through a psychological process of healing. However, the counselor also knows that a person with a complex disorder, such as PTSD, will also need a trained clinical specialist who is specially trained in the discipline of the veteran's disorder. With this knowledge, the counselor may have to suggest to the veteran that he should be treated by a different counselor or therapist who works specifically within his psychological discipline. This is an important fact that may assist the veteran to come out of the emotional wilderness.

Military personnel immediately learn that there are two important personnel positions in the military. The doctors and chaplains will be with the troops in peace time and on the battlefields. Both of these positions provide a service. One is to save your physical life and the other your emotional and spiritual life. It is important that the chaplain's position be defined. Whether you are on active duty or on inactive status, you can always approach a chaplain for guidance and counseling.

I am an ordained Christian chaplain who will refer to Christian counseling, when dealing with the military, as spiritual counseling.

Whether military or civilian, a chaplain is committed to his chaplaincy and functions as a servant to all in the military.

Psychological therapy will help the veterans with their post traumatic stress disorder (PTSD) by identifying and changing or replacing negative and irrational thoughts and memories of a traumatic event associated with their anxieties.

CHAPTER 9

THE DEPARTMENT OF VETERANS AFFAIRS

(Always have a veteran service officer (VSO) working with and for you. The following benefits and requirements are subject to change according to the revisions of the US Government)

ABOUT THE DEPARTMENT OF VETERANS AFFAIRS

The Department of Veterans Affairs assists veterans with service connected disabilities in preparing for a new career and/or in finding suitable employment. They also offer services to the veterans to improve their ability to live as self-supporting and productive members of society.

In 1636, the American and English colonies in North America, provided pensions for disabled war veterans. In 1789, the first Congress assumed the burden of also paying disabled veterans benefits. This was enacted with the ratification of the US Constitution.

It is important to understand that the benefits listed in this chapter were earned by you, the veteran and your family. It is also important for you to understand what the requirements are for those benefits to be awarded. An honorable and general discharge will qualify a veteran for most VA benefits. However, a dishonorable and bad conduct discharge issued through a general court-martial may eliminate a veteran from his or her VA benefits.

The following is a brief glimpse into the benefits that the US Department of Veterans Affairs, (DVA) has to offer to its veterans and their families.

- Health care benefits.
- Disability compensation.
- Pensions.
- Vocational rehabilitation and employment services.
- Education and training.
- Home loan guarantees.
- Life insurance.
- Veteran's mortgage life insurance.
- Burial benefits
- Death pensions.
- Dependents Education Women's veteran's benefits.
- Homeless veteran's benefits.
- Small and disadvantaged business benefits.
- Workplace benefits.
- State employment services.
- Loans for farms and homes.
- Naturalization preferences.
- Federal tax credits and assistance.
- Availability of armed forces retirement homes.
- Death gratuity.

The aforementioned are only a few benefits provided by the DVA with the proper eligibility.

WHO IS ELIGIBLE?

Veterans may be eligible for DVA health care benefits. In addition the following persons may also be eligible:

- A veteran's dependent
- A surviving spouse or child of a deceased veteran
- A member of the US Military Reserves or National Guard
- An active duty military service member
- Prisoners of War: Former prisoners of war who were incarcerated for at least 30 days are entitled to a presumption of service connection for disabilities.

There are also a number of countries, wartime service organizations and special groups that assisted the USA by providing military related services during times of war Check with the DVA for guidance regarding benefit status and organizations, countries involved.

SPECIFIC DVA BENEFITS

The Department of Veterans Affairs has programs which can be designed specifically for an individual with disabilities. When I needed assistance, I was directed to the DVA Independent Living Program. This program allowed me to meet my goals of becoming a Chaplain. The DVA structured a program allowing me to meet my educational needs and provided me with skills in chaplaincy and Biblical counseling. Because of the benefits provided to me and my family, I have become a very active member of my community and live a comfortable life style.

When you are awarded a disability rating, understand there are many DVA programs suitable for your needs. You must take the time to research to determine what the DVA has to offer.

In this chapter, I barely touched on the benefits offered by the DVA, who is eligible for what program and if there are limitations. The DVA will discuss, in detail, all of their programs and, even more importantly, what is available for you and your family.

HEALTH CARE

To enter the health care system a veteran must apply to enroll into the system. If a veteran has a Department of Veterans Affairs rating of 50% or more, service connected disability, he or she may be eligible with the approval of the DVA. The DVA can provide a manual, "Federal Benefits for Veterans" or an email address for all who are eligible.

The DVA provides a number of health care services; hospital, outpatient medical, dental, pharmacy and prosthetic services, domiciliary, nursing home, and community-based residential care, sexual trauma counseling, specialized health care for women veterans, health and rehabilitation programs for homeless veterans, readjustment counseling, alcohol and drug dependency treatment, medical evaluation for military service exposure including, Agent Orange, radiation, or other environmental hazards.

DISABILITY BENEFITS

The DVA administers have two disability programs. Both pay monthly benefits to disabled veterans.

- Disability Compensation: Veterans can pay you compensation if you are at least 10% disabled as a result of your military service (service-connected disability).
- Disability Pension: Can pay you a pension if you are a war-time veteran with limited income, unable to work or you are age 65 or older.

EDUCATION AND TRAINING

The DVA pays benefits to eligible veterans, dependents, reservists, and service members while they are in an approved training program. DVA major programs are:

- Montgomery GI Bill
- Veterans' Educational Assistance Program (VEAP)
- Survivors' & Dependents' Educational Assistance

Vocational Rehabilitation & Employment

- Job Search
- Vocational Evaluation
- Career Exploration
- Vocational Training
- Education Training
- Rehabilitation Service

Burial Benefits

- Headstones and Markers
- Presidential Memorial Certificate (PMC)
- Burial Flag
- Reimbursement of Burial Expenses
- Burial in a VA National Cemetery

Dependents' and Survivors' Benefits

- Dependency and Indemnity Compensation (DIC)
- Death Pension
- VA Civilian Health and Medical Program (CHAMPVA)

Home Loans

The DVA offer's a number of home loan services to eligible veterans, some military personnel, and certain spouses.

- Guaranteed Loans Refinancing
- Loans
- Special Grants

Life Insurance

- Service members' Group Life Insurance (SGLI)
- Veterans' Group Life Insurance (VGLI)
- Service-Disabled Veterans Insurance

(Each DVA benefit has its own eligibility requirements.)

CHAPTER 10

A PERSONAL SUMMATION

"And He shall judge the world in righteousness; He shall minister judgment to the people in uprightness."
Ps. 9:8 KJV

I feel that it is important that I provide the reader with a factual case history of a person who has gone through both military and civilian careers and the Department of Veterans Affairs disability process. I am referring to my background and the reasons that my wife and I decided to write this book.

I am a Vietnam veteran, a 3rd Marine Division, United States Marine Corps, who served in-country from 1967 through1968. I went through the "Tet Offensive." It was during that time that I was "medevac'd" out-of-country and diagnosed with acute anxieties, which is known today as PTSD.

I was sent to a mental hospital in Okinawa, Japan, for approximately 8 weeks and was then told I could return home with a medical discharge under honorable conditions. Because of the social situation in the US at that time, I knew that if I, as a Black man, returned home even with an honorable discharge I would face formidable odds finding a job

(1968). I decided to return to the war because I felt it would be more honorable to die serving my country. I returned to Vietnam to the same combat area. I did not know that I was suffering with PTSD.

Within a few months, I was thrown from, or blown out of, a military truck. I have never been sure of exactly what happened. All I remember is flying through the air and being hit by the truck's door which had also flown off with me. I don't know how long I was unconscious, but I woke up in a hospital and was unable to walk. Today, a veteran blown out of a vehicle may be diagnosed with a traumatic brain injury, (TBI).

However, the incident in the truck had caused physical damage to my left leg. Today, 49 years later, I still have a deep indentation in my leg where the door hit me. Every once in a while my leg goes numb and won't hold my weight. Because of the leg problem, I keep a cane in each car and in my home. Even though I very seldom need to use it for support, I have had the occasion when it was necessary.

I took the time to write of the aforementioned physical injuries and emotional stresses I experienced for you so that you could understand what you are going through is very real and not just in your head. When applying for DVA disability, it is important to relate the truth, and to your military medical records to support your claim(s). However, in my case, I was denied benefits three times before I was awarded a disability rating.

That is when I learned that if the DVA can frustrate you by denying your claim they can cause you to lose interest and drop your claim. The benefit to the government is just another veteran who will not receive his or her disability benefits for the rest of his or her life. If you could total every claim dropped by a frustrated veteran in a year you could probably support a small country. As far as the government is concerned, it is about money, not your health.

The danger of a veteran with PTSD being denied his or her benefits is that is exacerbates their personal situation and can send the veteran over the edge. It may cause a deep depression, homelessness, cause a rage that may lead to murder or, in some cases, suicide.

When I returned from Vietnam, my first wife told me that I was different. At the time, we did not know this was a possible signal relating to PTSD. In those days, the government had not yet coined that term nor had it acknowledged that veterans could have a psychological disorder. In the 1980's, the term Post Traumatic Stress Disorder (PTSD) was given to veterans from Vietnam who were having emotional problems.

I returned from Vietnam with a rage growing inside of me and needed an outlet. I became a Deputy Sheriff and worked undercover for years. This provided me with an outlet for my rage without breaking the law, so it was a safe zone for me. However, because of that rage, I could not deal with micro-management, and certainly not incompetent leadership. I also had a short fuse and, over the span of the next 25 years had the following careers: Deputy Sheriff undercover, patrol cop, Public Defender Investigator, was a US Government international operative; a California State licensed private investigator and an employee of Northrop Grumman working in at least 7 different departments. A symptom of PTSD is becoming bored and changing jobs frequently, and having difficulty with management. The true problem was within myself, not with others.

The type of jobs that I pursued was to validate myself while becoming an over-achiever. It was explained to me by a VA psychiatrist that my over-achieving was my answer to remaining busy with new positive thoughts and actions to avoid sliding into the negative of boredom and possible depression. For almost 35 years I stayed about as far away from anything military as I could. I did not realize that those actions, along with what I shared above, indicated that I had PTSD. After so many years, though, my legs and ankles were getting worse. However, I still did nothing about my situation until I had friend after friend telling me that I should go to the DVA regarding my symptoms, which were becoming worse. When I started my journey, I knew nothing of the DVA and the benefits that were available. I insisted that I had no problems and wanted nothing to do with the government disability system. My attitude was that since I had both of my arms and legs and a functional brain then there was nothing wrong with me.

When I finally went to the VA Hospital, they directed me to an office that had a number of veteran representatives who were not affiliated with the government but were there to help me. They included the VFW, the DAV and LA County and they were there to help me apply for my benefits.

My journey started, and that beginning included being completely examined by the VA Hospital to determine the extent of my physical disabilities. I was also sent to the VA Hospital to a psychiatrist to evaluate my emotional stability and to explain the diverse types of emotional disorders, which included PTSD. That was the first time I had heard of PTSD, and I learned about it as I was being told that I suffered from that disorder. It was now that I began to understand the depth of my disorder.

In today's prison system, there are many in custody who are is charged with violent crimes including murder. Many of them are men who fought in our wars but who had no knowledge of their disabilities and/or emotional disorders. They tried to warn those people around them who were, unfortunately, ill-equipped to deal with what they were hearing and experiencing.

If you are a veteran of a war and you have instant violent thoughts, you most likely have PTSD. When a person verbally attacks you, or attempts to put you down by character assassination or lying about you, you may turn to violence or murder to shut their mouths permanently.
"When my father and my mother forsake me, then the Lord will take me up." Ps. 27:10 KJV

I am a divorced Black man who re-married a Jewish woman. We have always been happy with each other, but her family members made it a point to attempt to break us up. All of the members of her family were engaged in a 12-year brutal attack against the both of us to break us up. It was during this period of time when I realized that I was capable of violently hurting someone or going to jail for killing someone. I also realized that no-one in her family was worth going to jail for so I had to control myself. This battle had been more difficult than my time spent in the Vietnam War. However, God was on my side in my battle against evil, as He usually is.

I could handle this dangerous period of time in my life by replacing my negative thoughts with positive ones. I went to graduate school and studied psychotherapy and religious counseling. This action allowed me to better understand how not to burden myself with the psychological disorders and anger of the people attacking me. I learned how not to personalize the negative thoughts and actions of others. I continued my education and became an ordained Christian minister. After that, true to my philosophy of over-achieving, I returned to school to become a chaplain.

I went to a government funded and GI Bill approved university, graduate level and earned my Masters and Doctorate. I am now a Christian Minister and both my wife and I are Christian Chaplains, dedicated to helping veterans.

I filled my mind with positives based on the Bible and God's love for His people. This move may have saved my life and the lives of my angry, and angered, in-laws. My wife is everything positive in my life. She is a retired high school teacher, a counselor, an accomplished oil painter, a professional writer and a chaplain. Together, we can keep each other in the positive because she also has PTSD. She has paid the price for the emotional abuse, the family wars and attacks that she endured at the hands of her family.

It does not take a combat situation on foreign soil to cause an emotional disorder. However, it does take a strong support system and faith in God to handle your emotional disorder.

I fought for three to four years to obtain the DVA benefits that I earned. Today, we are retired and live off our retirement pension, social security and DVA disability benefits.

Remember, when applying for your DVA benefits, you will become frustrated. Continue to appeal for your benefits until you receive the disability rating you deserve. The benefits are not about the money. It is about receiving assistance for your physical disabilities and emotional disorders. The DVA will assist you in living a comfortable, meaningful and productive life. That is the goal of the DVA for those who continue to present factual, helpful information when applying for your benefits.

My wife and I pray that this book will provide the information to warriors, spouses, children and anyone who can use this information to help all veterans. Also, please always remember to keep God as your companion. You cannot fail because He will not let you.

BIBLICAL SCRIPTURES
(KING JAMES VERSION)

This chapter is to assist in comforting veterans who are going through the frustration of the Department of Veterans Affairs disability process and who are dealing with emotional problems.

Comfort – Numbers 14:9, Deuteronomy 31:6, Psalm 27:10; 46:7; 73:23; 94:14; 103:17; Isaiah 41:17; Matthew 28:20; John 6:37-39; Romans 8:38-39

Peace – Exodus 33:14; Numbers 6:24-26; Psalm 85:8; 119:165; 62:11; 72:13; 142:3; 147:6, Isaiah 26:3; 32:17; 57:2; 57:15, Jeremiah 10:6, Habakkuk 3:19, 2 Corinthians 12:9, Ephesians 3:16

Despair – Psalm 46:1; 100:5, 119:116, Isaiah 51:6, Jeremiah 32:17, Ezekiel 34:16, Daniel 2:23, Matthew 11:29-30, John 14:27, Romans 5:1-2; Ephesians 2:14, Colossians 3:15

Fear – Deuteronomy 1:17; 7:21, 1 Chronicles 16:25-26, Nehemiah 4:14, Psalm 4:8; 28:7; 56:3, Proverbs 16:6, Isaiah 35:4; 41:10, Jeremiah 15:20, Joel 3:16, 2 Corinthians 1:10, Philippians 4:9 Haggai 2:4, Ephesians 1:18, 2 Thessalonians 3:3, Hebrews 10:35, James 1:12

Grief – Psalm 34:7; 71:20-21; 116:15; 119:28; 119:50; 121:5-8, Isaiah 43:2, 2 Corinthians 1:3-4

Times of Trouble – Psalm 9:12; 43:7, Hebrews 13:6

Anxiety – Genesis 28:15, Job 34:12, Psalm 20:7; 50:15; 55:22; 68:19; 86:7, Proverbs 3:5-6, Isaiah 40:11; 41:13, Matthew 11:28, John 16:33

For Those Who Feel Weak – 1 Chronicles 16:11, Psalm 37:10-11; Psalm 55-15; 37:39-40; 46:1; 50:15; 121:5-8, 138:7, John 16:33

Feeling Desperate and Depressed – Psalm 30:5; 34:18; 40:1-2; 42:11; 126:5, Zephaniah 3:17, John 10:10.

Hope -

Biblical Counseling should place emphasis on "Hope." The role of "Hope" in the process of sanctification should never be underestimated. Consider what scripture says about its many contributions to that process. Biblical Hope produces;

- Joy (Proverbs 10:28; Rom. 5:2-3; 12:12; 1 Thess. 4:13)
- Confidence (2 Cor. 3:12; Phil. 1:20)
- Perseverance (Rom. 8:24-25)
- Effective Ministry (2 Cor. 4:8-18)
- Faith and Love (Col. 1:4-5)
- Consistency (1 Thess. 1:3)
- Energy and Enthusiasm (1 Tim. 4:10)
- Stability (Heb. 6:19)
- An intimate relationship with God (Heb. 7:19)
- Personal purity (1 John 3:3)

The Bible places such emphasis on the role of hope, in spiritual growth, that it must be a strong emphasis in biblical counseling as well.

When reading the aforementioned scriptures, read the complete chapter to receive the full spiritual blessings and understanding of how the verse is to be interpreted.

When I went through my ordeal with my aliments, disabilities and psychological problems, I always remembered that I was not alone, because **"God is my companion."**

All scriptures used in this book are from: "King James Version".

GLOSSARY OF APPEALS, DEPARTMENT OF VETERANS AFFAIRS

(This glossary contains many of the terms commonly used in the appeal process.)

Advance on the Docket - A change in the order in which an appeal is reviewed and decided, from the date when it would normally occur to an earlier date.

Appellant – A person who has appealed a local VA office claim determination.

Associate Counsel - See Counsel.

Board - The Board of Veterans Appeals

Board of Veterans Appeals - The section of the VA that reviews benefit claims appeals and issues decisions on those appeals.

Board Member - An attorney appointed by the Secretary of Veterans Affairs and approved by the President of the U.S. to decide veteran benefits appeals.

BVA - Abbreviation of Board of Veterans Appeals.

BVA Hearing - A personal hearing held at the BVA office in Washington, DC, or at a local VA office, that is conducted by a Board member. These hearing can also be held by video conference from some regional' offices.

Claim - A request for veterans' benefits.

Claim Number - A number assigned by the VA that identifies a person who has filed a claim; often called a "C-number." The VA now uses the veteran's Social Security number for its purpose, but older files still bear the "C-number."

Claims File or Claims Folder - The file containing all documents concerning a veteran's claim.

Counsel - Counsel and Associate Counsel are attorneys skilled in veterans' law who assist Board members in preparing decisions. They are like law clerks that help judges.

Decision - The product of the BVA's review of an appeal. A decision might, for example, grant or deny the benefit or benefits claimed, or remand the case back to the local VA office for additional action.

Determination – A decision on a claim made by a local VA office.

Docket - A listing of appeals that have been filed with the BVA. Appeals are listed in numerical order, called docket number order, based on when a VA Form 9 is received by the local VA office.

File - To submit written material, usually by mailing it or delivering it in person.

Issue - Something specific you want the Board to grant you when it reviews your appeal. For example, if you filed an appeal asking the Board to grant you service connections for a heart disorder and a knee disability, and grant you a higher disability rating for an already service-connected shoulder (OLDER?) disability, the appeal would be said to contain three issues.

Motion - A legal term used to describe a request that the Board take some specific action in processing your appeal (such as advance your case on the docket), or that it give you permission to do something concerning your appeal (such, as send in evidence late in the appeal process). The Board's "Rules of Practice" tell you when a motion is required, what a particular motion should include and where you should file it. Most motions must be in writing.

Motion to Advance on the Docket - A request that the BVA review and decide an appeal sooner than it normally would for a specific reason.

Motion to Reconsider - A request for the BVA to review (reconsider) its decision on an appeal.

NOD- Abbreviation for Notice of Disagreement

Notice of Disagreement - A written statement saying that you disagree with a local VA office's determination on your claim and that you want to appeal that determination.

Personal Hearing - A meeting, similar to an interview, between an appellant and a VA official who will decide an appellant's case, during which testimony and other evidence supporting the case, will be presented. There are two types of personal hearings: local office hearings (also called regional office hearings or hearing officer hearings) and BVA hearings.

Remand - The action the Board takes in returning an appeal to the local VA office where the claim originated. This action is taken when something else needs to be done before the Board can make a decision in an appeal.

Representative - Someone familiar with the VA's benefit claim process that assists claimants in the preparation and presentation of an appeal. Most representatives are Veterans Service Organization employees who specialize in veteran's benefit claims. Other individuals such as lawyers may also serve as representative.

Simultaneously Contested Claim - A simultaneously contested claim is a claim where more than one person is trying to get a VA benefit or status that only one of them can have. Examples might be two people each damming they are entitled to all of the proceeds of the same life insurance policy, or two people each asking to be recognized as a particular veteran's lawful surviving spouse.

SOC - Abbreviation for Statement of the Case.

Statement of the Case - This is a document prepared by the local VA office processing your appeal. It gives you a summary of the evidence considered in your case, a listing of the laws and regulations used to decide your claim, and an explanation of why the local VA office decided your claim as it did. Reviewing the sac will help you prepare your substantive appeal.

Substantive Appeal - Normally, a completed VA Form 9.

SSOC - Abbreviation for Supplemental Statement of the Case.

Supplemental Statement of the Case - An update to an SOC prepared when the VA receives new evidence, or a new issue is added to an appeal, after the SOC was prepared.

Testimony - This is the legal term used to describe what you and others who know about the facts of your case (witnesses) say at a hearing. Basically, to "testify" at a BVA hearing just means to tell what you know about your case. VA hearings are much more informal than court hearings, so you don't need to worry about technical rules of evidence or being cross-examined when you testify.

Travel Board Hearing - A personal hearing conducted at a local VA Office by a Board member.

United States Court of Appeals For Veterans Claims - An independent Federal court that reviews appeals of BVA decisions

VA Form 9 - You receive this VA form, titled "Appeal to the Board of Veterans Appeals," with the SOC. It is the form you fill out and file with the local VA Office to complete your appeal.

Veterans Service Organization (VSO) - A non-profit organization that represents the interests of veterans for free. Most VSOs have specific membership criteria, although membership is not usually required to obtain assistance with benefit claims and appeals. Your local VA office can provide information about VSOs serving your area.

GLOSSARY OF BIBLICAL, CLINICAL PSYCHOLOGICAL AND PROBLEMATIC STRESS TERMS

Acute: extremely great or serious; crucial

Anxiety: distress or uneasiness of mind caused by fear of danger or misfortune; a state of apprehension and psychic tension.

Biblical Counselor: A Christian/Biblical counselor and or therapist are specialist in counseling through the biblical word and secular clinical counseling. However, he also knows that a person with a complex disorder may also need a trained clinical specialist whose is specially trained in the discipline of the client's disorder. It is about counselors who know when to talk and when not to talk. It is also about the counselor who practices biblical and wise counseling with the right motives, always using scriptures as his or her guide.

Biblical Counseling: Biblical Counseling is based on the convictions that (1) God's Word should be our counseling authority, (2) counseling is a part of the basic discipline ministry of the local church, and (3) God's people can and should be trained to counseling effectively. Biblical Counseling is counseling from a biblical perspective.

Chaplain: An ecclesiastic attached to the chapel of a royal court, college, etc. or to a military unit, also a person who says the prayers, invocation, etc. for an organization or at an assembly.

Clergy: The clergy is a group or body of ordained persons in a religion as distinguished from the laity.

Cognitive: pertaining to the mental processes of perception, memory, judgment and reasoning as contrasted with emotional and volitional processes.

Cognitive Psychology: the branch of psychology studying the mental processes involved in perception, learning, memory and reasoning.

Cognitive Therapy: a form of therapy for depression in which the goal is to diminish symptoms by correcting distorted thinking based on negative self-perception and expectation; also called cognitive behavior therapy.

Counseling: Professional guidance in resolving personal conflicts and emotional problems.

Crisis: A crucial situation, the turning point in a disease, when it becomes clear whether the patient will recover.

Depression: a condition of general emotional dejection and withdrawal; sadness greater and more prolonged than that warranted by any objective reason.

Disorder: A disturbance in physical or mental health or functions; malady or dysfunction.

Emotion: an affective state of consciousness in which joy, sorrow, fear, hate, or the like is experienced as distinguished from cognitive and volitional states of consciousness.

Emotional: Actuated, effected, or determined by emotion rather than reason: An emotional decision is often a wrong decision.

Expository Preaching: Expository Preaching is the nature of exposition; serving to expound, set forth, or explain. Expository Preaching is the communication of a biblical concept, derived from transmitted through a historical, grammatical and literary study of a passage in its context, which the Holy Spirit first applies to the personality and experience of the preacher then through the preacher, applies to the listener.

Minister: A person authorized to conduct religious worship; members of the clergy. A person authorized to administer sacraments, as at Mass.

Pastor: A minister or priest in charge of a church and having spiritual care of a number of persons.

Psychological: Pertaining to, dealing with, or affecting the mind, esp. as a function of awareness, feeling, or motivation.

Rehabilitation: the restoration to a condition of good health; ability to work or the like.

Self-esteem: a realistic respect for or favorable impression of oneself; self-respect and or an inordinately or exaggeratedly favorable impression of oneself.

Spiritual: Pertaining to the spirit or soul, as distinguished from the physical nature: a spiritual approach to life.

Stress: a specific response by the body to a stimulus, such as fear or pain, which disturbs or interferes with the normal physiological equilibrium of an organism; a physical, mental or emotional strain or tension.

Syndrome: a predictable characteristic pattern of behavior, action, etc., that tends to occur under certain circumstances.

Trauma: an experience that produces psychological injury or pain; a psychological injury so caused.

Wisdom: The quality or state of being wise; knowledge of what is true or right coupled with just judgment as to action; sagacity, discernment, or insight.

REFERENCES

1 "The Marine's Bible," Holman Bible Publishers, Nashville, Tennessee, Copyright 2004, ISBN 1-58640-104-1, page vii

2 Internet, "Board of Veteran's Appeals Ombudsman" (Customer Service): Complaints, Questions, Concerns, etc., www.va.gov/vbs/bva/contactbva.htm

3 Ibid – "Board of Veteran's Appeals Ombudsman"

4 Internet, "Veterans Affairs Department – Board of Veterans' Appeals, Board of Contract Appeals, Health Services, Veterans Benefits, Compensation and Pension." http://Law.jrank.org/pages/11095/veterans-affairs-department.html

5 Ibid – "Veterans Affairs Department"

6 Ibid – "Veterans Affairs Department"

7 "The Post Traumatic Stress Disorder Sourcebook"
Authors: Glenn R. Schiraldi, PhD,
Lowell House Publishing, Los Angeles, CA.
ISBN 0-07373-0265-8   Copyright 2000, Pages 348 thru 359

8 Ibid - "The Post Traumatic Stress Disorder Sourcebook," Pages 348-359

9 **"Counseling for Post-Traumatic Stress Disorder,"** (London: sage, 1992), M.J. Scott and S.G. Stradling, page 28

10 **"The Post Traumatic Stress Disorder Sourcebook"**
Authors: Glenn R. Schiraldi, PhD, Lowell House Publishing, Los Angeles, CA.

11 **"The American Heritage – Stedman's Medical Dictionary,"** 2nd edition, Houghton Mifflin Company (Publisher), New York, copyright 2004
ISBN 0-618-42899-2, Page 838

12 **"The PTSD Workbook,"** Mary Beth Williams, PhD, and Soili Poijula PhD

13 Internet study **"Brain Differences in Vets of 1991 War,"** by E.J. Mundell – Gannett News Service, posted: Wednesday, May 2, 2007 (6:22:42 EDT)
www.navytimes.com/news/2007/05/gns_gulfwarvets.

14 Internet study **"Gulf War Syndrome Doesn't Exist,"** Associated Press, September 12, 2006, http://www.military.com/newscontent.htlm

15 **"Disabled American Veteran's Magazine,"** Article, "Agent Orange: Legacy of Disabilities," Author, Thom Wilborn (January/February 2005) pg 17

16 **The Stress of Life** Author, Hans Selye, M.D.
Mc Graw-Hill Company, New York, NY. USA
ISBN 07-056206-7 Copyright 1956, Preface page viii

17 Ibid - **"The Post Traumatic Stress Disorder Sourcebook,"** Pages 348-359

18 **Borderline Personality Disorder Demystified,** Arthur: Robert O. Friedel, MD, Published by: Marlowe & Company, 245 West 17th

Street, New York, NY, 10011 Copyright 2004, ISBN 1-56924-456-1, Page 55

19 **"Clinical Handbook of Psychological Disorders,"** Edited by David H. Barlow
The Guilford Press, 72 Spring Street, New York, NY 10012
Copyright 2001, ISBN 1-57230-611-4, pages 114-115

20 **"Cognitive Therapy Techniques in Christian Counseling,"**
Author: Mark R. McMinn, Ph.D., Word Publishing, Dallas, TX,
Copyright 1991, ISBN 0-8499-0876-0, page 15-16

21 Ibid - **"Cognitive Therapy Techniques in Christian Counseling,"**
Pages 15-16

22 **Psychogenesis** Author: Jack Ensign Addington
Devorss and Company Publisher
PO Box 550, Marina Del Rey, CA 90294
Copyright 1971 ISBN: 0-87516-672-5, page 1

23 **"The Male Stress Syndrome,"** Author, Georgia Witkin, PhD
Newmarket Press Copyright 1994
18 East 48th Street, New York, NY 10017
ISBN 1-55704-206-3 (hc), pages 4-5

24 **"The Female Stress Syndrome,"** Author, Georgia Witkin, Ph.D.
Newmarket Press, Copyright 1991
18 East 48th Street, New York, NY 10017
ISBN 1-55704-098-2 (Pb), page 27

25 **"Bringing the War Back Home: Mental Health Disorders Among 103 788 US Veterans Returning From Iraq and Afghanistan Seen at Department of Veterans Affairs Facilities."** Karen H. Seal, Daniel Bertenthal, Christian R. Miner, Saunak Sen, and Charles Marmar. Arch Intern Med. 2007; 167:476-482. Published online: Vol. 167 No. 5, March 12, 2007 written by: Catharine

Paddock, Writer: Medical News Today, Copyright: Medical News Today, www.medicalnewstoday.com/articles

26 Internet, www.state.sc.us/dhm/clinical/chronic.htm - This handout was developed by Charles R. Goldman, M.D. (revised 7/30/98)

27 Internet, "Veterans Affairs Department – Board of Veterans' Appeals, Board of Contract Appeals, Health Services, Veterans Benefits, Compensation and Pension." http://Law.jrank.org/pages/11095/veterans-affairs-department.html

28 Ibid - Internet, "Veterans Affairs Department" – Board of Veterans' Appeals, Board of Contract Appeals, Health Services, Veterans Benefits, Compensation and Pension."

All scriptures used in this book are from: The King James Version and New King James Version." Thomas Nelson has given written permission to use scripture/verses New King James Version.

CPSIA information can be obtained
at www.ICGtesting.com
Printed in the USA
FSOW01n0259260817
37848FS

9 781640 456099